WILL I NEED A
CARDIGAN?

Travels with the British Abroad

WILL I NEED MY CARDIGAN?

Travels with the British Abroad

love
Cicely

Cicely Taylor

For My Family

Contents

Many of the stories told here actually happened, but not to the people described or in quite the way I have told them. A few people may recognise themselves, but only if they were specially nice or specially brave.

Introduction

It is three o'clock in the morning. I am sitting in the corridor outside a lavatory on a night-train in the middle of Wallachia. On one side of me the Romanian guide is in tears, and on the other a rather tipsy clergyman is reading The Odyssey (in Greek). Every carriage is packed with people and the occasional goat. All around is drinking and shouting and singing.

How did I, delicately bred to arrange flowers and make cucumber sandwiches for charity tea-parties, find myself in this ludicrous situation?

It goes back to an approach from the Walking Czar of a travel empire called Serenissima. He knew I could climb a hill and he needed a leader for a walk he had arranged in Burgundy.

My husband egged me on: it might make me more interesting; after all I had hardly been abroad in my life.

I went to France to discover the route and then, feeling anything but confident, met the walkers – a group of Australians – at Heathrow. Their first question at least was encouraging: "Is it cheaper to buy champagne here or in France?" I guessed the answer.

Soon I was taking walks all over Europe, and sometimes shepherding coach tours and cruises – often with a Guest Lecturer, several times my husband.

Those were the days of the amateur. No contracts, no training, no clip-boards and certainly no uniforms. It was all common sense and fingers crossed. There was one golden rule: do not fall out with the lecturer or guide.

After every tour I had to write a report. Most of them were very dull because the tours went so smoothly. Occasionally comic or dramatic things happened, and these I have turned into this book.

Cicely Taylor
June 2013

Leningrad
The Secret Policeman

~ January ~

Cast List

Mr and Mrs Hutchings	*Retired banker and magisterial wife*
Major Cramp	*Enjoyer from Wiltshire*
Mrs Melbury-Jones	*Remote descendent of the Romanovs*
Lady Palmer	*Dignified and stylish*
Mr Smith	*Quiet bachelor*
Tess and John	*Newly-engaged young couple*
Ms Wright	*Well-travelled vegetarian*
And others	

Russia in the nineteen-eighties was still in the grip of communism. Tours had to be organised through *Intourist*, the state-owned company. Hotels were dreary, there were very few restaurants, and guides were hard as nails. You were given an itinerary and stuck to it – only to find that every other tour had exactly the same itinerary, at the same time. On the other hand tours were cheaper and travellers were less demanding. What most struck the visitor was the contrast between the lavishly restored buildings and the bedraggled people. At the same time the black-market was in full swing, almost everyone on the streets was prepared to sell things illicitly and it was easy to bribe officials with a few packets of cigarettes.

Thursday: Gatwick – Moscow – Leningrad

I am on the train to Gatwick and I wish I wasn't. It is early morning – most of my fellow travellers are slumped over seats or suitcases, and I am wide awake having been up since four o'clock. I have led many, many tours, but I'm always nervous at the start: will the flight be delayed, will everyone turn up, will someone be bumped off the plane, will there be an agent or guide to meet us, and above all will the clients be difficult?

And here is Mrs Melbury-Jones, a direct descendant of the Empress Catherine the Great she tells us all. Though small and dumpy like Napoleon, she clearly means to be the Empress of this tour.

We already have all the makings of a good drama. Our flight tickets are handed out by an official at Gatwick and are clearly marked Moscow. Our flight to Leningrad doesn't exist and nobody at the airport can tell us why.

It is still very early in the morning and I telephone my travel company's emergency number. "Oh, sorry, we should have told you. We couldn't get a direct flight, so you must pick up the connection at Moscow." Thanks a lot.

There is nothing for it – we will have to fly to Moscow and hope for the best. I try and reassure the nervous clients, feeling far from confident myself. Goodness knows where we will end up.

We do land at Moscow – a slight relief – but the airport is dismal. It is a large, concrete building with a tin roof, dim lighting, and freezing cold – probably an old hanger.

"Call this an aerodrome?" booms Mr Hutchings – a big man, rather formally dressed – dark coat with a velvet collar, red carnation in buttonhole, rolled umbrella under arm. His wife is in a fur coat smelling strongly of moth-balls. She is feeling faint and asks for water. Some hope.

I grab a handful of customs declaration forms which we have to fill in in duplicate, stating everything of value we are bringing into the Soviet Union. One copy has to be kept, and shown on leaving the country. The officials glare at us and, heaving with reluctance, slowly stamp forms and passports.

Thank goodness there is a guide waiting. Svetlana: middle-aged, grey-faced and scowling. Clearly she would rather be somewhere else. (Not the only one). We will have a tour of Moscow and catch a late plane to Leningrad.

Everyone except me cheers up. I know there will be more problems and I am right. Svetlana tells me quietly, not without pleasure, that our hotel in Leningrad burnt down this morning.

We drive through the streets of Moscow, Svetlana giving out information in a flat, bored voice. At Red Square we stop at St Basil's cathedral, and admire the onion domes, towers and pointed gables that dominate the red brick building, built by Ivan the Terrible to celebrate his victory over the Tartars.

We pass on to Lenin's mausoleum, set against the wall of the Kremlin, guarded by goose-stepping soldiers in thick grey overcoats. Svetlana won't let us off the bus, which pleases me as I know everyone would scatter in all directions and be difficult to round up. We end up at a hotel for tea served in thick white cups – every one with the handle broken off. "Cups never had handles in the eighteenth century," says Mrs Melbury-Jones.

Back to the airport, and a long wait for our flight to Leningrad. We land in the not-so-early hours of the morning. Another dreary aerodrome for Mr Hutchings and another long wait for our luggage.

Our new guide, Galina, is waiting for us. So much depends on guides, how well they speak English and whether they have a good clear voice, for a start. Eastern European ones, usually women, are trained to roll out boring statistics and facts about their country, while Arab men resent interference from a woman, which can make the job difficult. Galina is as large and bossy as Svetlana, but thank goodness a bit smilier.

I tell the group that we are going to stay in a different hotel and that this often happens with *Intourist*, and one just accepts it. Best not to tell them the reason quite yet.

Instead of the Leningrad Hotel – conveniently placed near the centre of the city, we have a long drive to a monstrous, concrete building, miles high, standing beside the Gulf of Finland, looking out on a cold, concrete sea. It could have been worse: at least there are enough rooms to go round – not always the case in Leningrad. I wait downstairs in case there are any complaints, and watch the local prostitutes hanging around outside trying to slip past the doormen – or rather guards – into the hotel.

At the end of every corridor there is a grim-faced woman, dressed in black sitting and knitting and glaring. Woe betide any loose female caught trying to sneak past her.

Friday: Leningrad

By 4.30am I am in bed, and four hours later arrive down at breakfast to find the whole party tucking into semolina, bread and jam, washed down with weak tea – all ready for a day's sightseeing.

It is a dismal morning, raining steadily with the snow in the streets melting to grey slush. Galina is dressed in bright colours, unlike most of the Russian women, who wear shapeless coats and headscarves, stomping along with heads down. Everyone is impressed by the beautiful buildings and clean streets absent of traffic, but unimpressed by stinking diesel fumes coming from every *Intourist* bus lined up outside the tourist sites.

Our first port of call is the Peter and Paul fortress, built as a sea-defence for Peter the Great by Russian forced labour and Swedish prisoners. It was never used for its original purpose because the real sea defence of St Petersburg was the navy – with its fleet based at Kronstadt out in the Gulf of Finland. During the war, however, the Nazis advanced on land, and Leningrad was the victim of a vicious siege that began in September 1941 and lasted for 900 days. By the end, over 600,000 people had died of starvation or sickness.

Outside the fortress there is a group of music students with brass instruments and as we approach they strike up the Grand March from *Aida*, followed by the British National Anthem. Mr Hutchings (Aerodrome), still in his smart overcoat with fading carnation, makes us all stand self-consciously to attention, hands by the side, fists clenched.

Inside the fortress we visit the church where most of the Czars have been buried – its thin gilded spire one of the landmarks of the city. Galina tells us that it is possible that the ill-fated Nicholas II and Alexandra may eventually be buried here.

We walk round the huge bare building with its cold marble tombs – Mrs Melbury-Jones struts in front, patting each one as we pass. "My ancestors, you know." It may be her first visit to Russia but she feels proprietorial about "my family." Peter the Great's tomb is the only one allowed flowers on it – the one touch of colour to the gloomy interior.

The river Neva flows past the fortress, and we lean over the parapet watching hardy Russians breaking the ice and diving into the freezing water. Galina points out significant buildings across the river, but Aerodrome is more interested in chatting to his neighbour from Wiltshire, Major Cramp. "Is your new son-in-law satisfactory?" he asks. "Owns a grouse-moor and a stretch on the Tweed." Aerodrome nods. What more could one want?

Tess and John, a good-looking couple, are about forty years younger than the rest of the party, who treat them like naughty children. They are not too hot on culture, having come on this trip mainly to stock up on black-market caviar for their engagement party. They are taking this job seriously, holding hands and lagging behind while keeping a sharp look-out for likely sellers dodging from behind trees or doorways.

There are no adequate restaurants in the city, so we go back to the hotel for lunch. The food is wheeled into the dining room on huge iron trolleys – plates of spam with mounds of grey, mashed potato and over-cooked cabbage, accompanied by a syrupy fruit drink – much improved when laced with vodka.

Ms Wright, is a little, twitching, woman with an unhealthy complexion and thin hair hanging in a limp fringe; she demands vegetarian food which is impossible here, so she settles for mashed potato and cabbage.

After lunch we set out in the coach again. We have a photo-stop at the famous Bronze Horseman, an equestrian statue of Peter the Great. The Major nudges Aerodrome.

"Didn't Catherine the Great have a bit of nookie with a horse?" Mrs Melbury-Jones glares at them. They have taken to mobbing her up, and are delighted that she rises every time.

We stop again at Peter's little hut – a wooden shack now encased in brick, built by Peter the Great so he could direct operations for the construction of the city – a marked contrast with the grand buildings all round.

Moored across the river we can see the cruiser Aurora – from where the blank shot was fired that started the revolution in 1917. On our other side we pass the still-smouldering Leningrad Hotel. "This is where we should have stayed," I say. Everyone is horrified – supposing we'd arrived twenty-four hours earlier?

At dinner the waiters open their jackets surreptitiously; rabbit hats tucked into linings, caviar from sleeves, lacquer boxes from pockets, amber necklaces from waistcoats, and army watches from trousers. Lady Palmer, family motto: "A mind conscious of rectitude," wheels and deals. Mrs Aerodrome (senior magistrate) in the thick of it. Tess and John are thrilled and stock up with caviar. Mr Smith from Rochdale takes no part: a tall man with strong features, who looks like Humphrey Bogarde, wearing a long fawn-coloured mackintosh tied with a belt at the waist.

Early bed for everyone. My telephone rings at intervals during the night with unknown male voices on the line. At last I twig and pull the telephone out of its socket.

Saturday: Pushkin and Pavlosk

Mrs Melbury-Jones, who feels she should be treated like royalty, asks for early morning tea in her room. Not likely, but there are small coffee shops on some of the landings, and if she is prepared to wait in a long queue she can have an early cuppa.

This morning we are going to Pushkin, a town of Imperial palaces, formerly known as Tsarkoye Selo, and about fifteen miles south of Leningrad. The town was developed as a summer resort for the grand and rich families of St Petersburg.

We will visit the site known as the Catherine Palace – once an Imperial residence. In the war the Nazis used it as a barracks and it was later blown up. Restoration work started in 1957 and now, apart from the "before and after" photographs in every room, you would never know. It has a 300 yard long façade facing the park, painted bright blue, with white columns and gold embellishments – quite overpowering.

We pull on felt slippers over our shoes and start our tour, slipping and sliding around the shiny wooden floors, walking through one room after another, practically blinded by the gold leaf. How can they restore the palace to this standard when the people are so poor, we ask each other?

Afterwards we walk round the grounds. They are very pretty in the snow, with summer houses and follies dotted round a lake. A troll jumps out from behind every building to sell us the usual rabbit hats, enamel boxes, and tins of caviar for Tess and John. Mr Smith from Rochdale looks on, smiling. "Why on earth isn't he joining in?" they say.

Pavlovsk is next. It is not far from Pushkin, but there are no restaurants here, so we have to trail back along the same road to our hotel for another dreary lunch, and then out again.

Everyone prefers Pavlosk to Pushkin. For a start it is built in a more familiar style by a Scottish architect, Charles Cameron. It is a yellow classical building topped with a low dome like a blancmange, built as a country house for Catherine. It is still pretty grand with several drawing rooms, studies, a billiard room, dancing room and a picture gallery on the first floor. When the Nazis were advancing in 1941 the curator was smart enough to bury many of the pictures and statues in the grounds, where they survived. In spite of the grandeur it has rather a homely feel about it. "I could really live here," says Vegetarian Wright. "My family did" sniffs Mrs Melbury-Jones. On our way back from Pavlosk Galina shows us the point at which the German advance was finally held in 1943.

Tonight we are going to the ballet at the Kirov theatre. I know what a scrum there is to get coats from the cloakroom afterwards, so tell everyone to leave their coats in the coach and dive quickly in before they die of cold.

Nureyev is dancing. One of his last ever performances and it is impossible to get tickets in one block, so everyone is scattered randomly throughout the theatre – some in the stalls, some in boxes at the side and some on wooden benches in the gods. John and Tess find themselves in the royal box. The hammer and sickle have replaced the Imperial Eagle, but the green and gold-decoration has lost none of its glamour, and the couple wave graciously to their fellow-travellers. Everyone has paid the same high price for their tickets and I anticipate trouble.

The Russian audience is dolled up to the nines, children in their best dresses, ribbons in their hair. They clap and cheer and chatter at the end of every dance and the performers smile and bow, bringing the ballet to a halt each time. Encores: bunches of flowers thrown on to the stage, standing ovation for Nureyev, and many curtain calls.

Our coach is waiting outside and we jump aboard – delighted that we haven't had to wait in the long queues for coats. But now the mood changes and there are complaints about the theatre seats. Those on wooden benches had spotted the rest of the party sitting comfortably in the stalls, and those sitting comfortably were jealous of Tess and John, of all people, lording it in the Imperial box – especially Mrs Melbury-Jones who considered it was her birthright to sit there. I try and tell them that this is the Soviet Union where nothing is fair, but there is a nasty silence all the way back. At the hotel I cheerfully suggest that we go and have a glass of Russian champagne. There is no reaction, so I go straight to the restaurant and order caviar and champagne and wait. It's not long before they all appear and the band strikes up. We are away.......

Sunday: Leningrad

Today is the Hermitage Museum – the day everyone has been looking forward to. The afternoon will be free, but they all insist they will want to spend the whole day looking at the world-famous collection, with its three million works of art including four thousand paintings.

The museum complex includes six historic buildings along the embankment of the Neva, with the Winter Palace, former residence of Russian Emperors, the most famous. The transition from palace to museum was begun by Catherine the Great when she built up her art collection from Western Europe, including buying Sir Robert Walpole's great collection from Houghton Hall in Norfolk.

We walk across the huge square, where Lenin's supporters rallied to attack the Palace in 1917, and join a long queue of tourists outside a dingy back entrance. From time to time the door opens a crack and small groups are admitted. All tourists have to be outside and waiting at the same time, while with the smallest amount of imagination by *Intourist* they could be given timed entries. It's typical of the bureaucracy here.

At last it is our turn. It is hot and airless inside and we trail behind Galina, through long passages and huge rooms containing classical antiquities, through the Armorial Hall, the Malachite room, the Nicholas Hall, on and on. We look at beautiful furniture and silver objects which are black with tarnish. "Why don't they clean it?" they say.

We admire a clock in the shape of a peacock with several ingenious mechanical animals perched around the face. "Made by your famous George Cox and presented to Catherine the Great," says Galina. "James Cox" corrects Mrs Melbury-Jones, showing off and embarrassing the guide. "Quite right" says Aerodrome loudly: "George Cox played for Sussex." The Major nods and Mrs Melbury-Jones glares.

After a couple of hours we reach the Old Masters and stand behind other groups all trying to look at the Intourist-selected Rembrandts plus two small Leonardo's. Then we walk up a steep staircase to the top floor to see the collection of Impressionists, where everyone is enchanted by the bright clean rooms and dazzling colours after the gloomy museum. But there is no café and nowhere to sit down, and after another hour we go back to the hotel for lunch. There is no more talk of staying on or a return visit.

Most of the party are exhausted and spend the afternoon lying down, but the more intrepid want to go to a service in the Holy Trinity church, in the Alexander Nevsky Monastery – one of the few churches where services are allowed – and visit the churchyard next door, where musicians and writers are buried. We decide to take the metro to the Nevsky Prospekt, once the grandest and most expensive street in the city, planned by Peter the Great as the beginning of a road to Moscow. It still has style – enormously wide, and lined with elegant five-story buildings – but there is no life behind the façades.

There is however a café here – the only one in St Petersburg – known as the Literary Café, and frequented by students. We go in hoping for a warm welcome, but in spite of two young violinists playing folk tunes in a corner, the lights are dim, the cakes are stale and there is the usual "babushka" glaring at us from behind the counter, creating an unfriendly atmosphere. It is not popular with Tess and John – no black-market caviar – so we don't stay long. Instead we dive down into the metro again, carefully counting the stops to make sure we get out at the right place, and we join a few old ladies in headscarves to form the congregation in the church. The rich, deep voices of the male choir resounding over the priest's intoning make it a memorable service.

Outside it is snowing and the ground is slippery. The cemetery is closed, but there is a guard outside in a heavy grey overcoat, stamping his feet to keep warm. We are shocked by how easy it is to get what you want by simple bribes, but delighted when he opens the gate in exchange for a couple of packets of cigarettes, and we slither around in the dark, hanging on to each other for support, giggling nervously, and try to read the great and romantic names on the tombstones: Tchaikovsky, Mussorgsky, Borodin, Rimsky-Korsakov.

Most want to go back to the hotel by the number 7 bus which goes all the way, but Lady Palmer would like a taxi so I go with her. She is an elegant woman with a thin face and thin, beaky nose: thin hair neatly arranged in a hair net. She lives in a vast house in the north of England with a garden that has made her famous. Tess and John can't resist imitating her upper-class, old-fashioned accent.

There is no sign of a taxi, so we flag down a private car. The driver is rather the worse for drink, and we sway dangerously over the icy roads. After a while he pulls into the kerb, looks furtively round, jumps out and opens the boot. Out come painted ornaments, gilt mirrors, lamp-stands and some gold-sprayed plaster putti.

Not quite to Lady Palmer's aristocratic taste, but she refuses everything graciously and hands him a few dollars. This just encourages him, and he stops every few yards and digs out more objects.

A free evening tonight and some of us are going to the circus. It is difficult to get tickets and I am feeling very pleased with myself as I have done a deal with a waiter, Sergei, from the hotel: he will be there waiting for us outside the entrance with cheap black-market tickets.

There are huge crowds outside the building and no sign of Sergei and no tickets available from any source. Suddenly the Major spots our ex-prime-minister, Edward Heath, accompanied by an entourage of security men and officials. He greets him like an old friend and asks if he has any tickets to spare. Mr Heath looks embarrassed and heaves his shoulders up and down, but one of the security men says "Of course," hands us out enough tickets to go round, and we sit in splendour in the best seats with all the V.I.Ps. Again the crowd is dressed up to the nines, cheering and laughing and clapping. It's funny that they are so dour during the day and so cheerful in the evening. There are wonderful acrobats doing impossible feats, and all sorts of performing animals including a porcupine, white rats, an elephant and a kangaroo. Our animal-loving compatriots don't approve. Did the Major really know Mr Heath? "Never met him in my life."

Monday: Peterhof – Gatwick

It is our last day. Our flight leaves in the evening and we have time to go to Petrodvorets – Peterhof as it used to be called. This long yellow-painted palace was built for Peter the Great, on a hill overlooking the Gulf of Finland. In summer the grounds are dotted with gold statues, fountains and pools and streams, but now the statues are wrapped up inside wooden boxes and the water is frozen, so we hurry inside hardly glancing at the gardens.

There are more silk-hangings, more white and gold. We walk through the state rooms, goggling at this lavishness, but the room we like best is Peter the Great's study lined with simple oak panelling and plain furniture, and on the shelves small models of boats that he has carved himself.

There is one restaurant near here so we don't have to trail back to our hotel for lunch. It is built of wood, in the style of a Swiss chalet, and there is singing and dancing and plenty to drink. We are given wooden rattles to whirl round in time to the music and we join in the singing, eat heartily and depart cheerfully. Aerodrome and the Major have already left and I soon see why. They are in a children's playground nearby, where, over-enlivened by too much vodka, they are swinging on the swings and sliding down the slides, laughing and shouting, much to the amazement of children standing nearby. I call them to order and we board the coach for the airport, driving down dreary streets bordered by concrete blocks of flats, made even more depressing with dim lighting from the windows showing up identical pale green interiors. We pass a tall building with a message flashing across the top of it in bright neon lights. "What does it say?" we ask Galina. "DO NOT WASTE ELECTRICITY."

At the airport we have to fill in forms saying what we are taking out of the country. This causes consternation as form-filling seems to be a problem for these well-travelled people. They ask me what their passport number is, where they live, and I wouldn't be surprised if they asked me what their names are. They know they are being looked after and have almost given up thinking for themselves.

I am worried by the amount of caviar that Tess and John have accumulated. Will they get it through customs? Someone has told them if it is wrapped in silver paper it won't show up on the x-ray, but it's nonsense because their bags are opened and the caviar exposed. Tess produces calculators and dollars, and the customs officer glances round, takes them and closes the bags without looking at her. Nobody else has a problem except Mr Smith from Rochdale whose bags are opened and gone through with a tooth-comb. He is the only one going back empty-handed.

When we get home he sends me a postcard. "I am in the police force – and not allowed to deal on the black market."

China
Big Wild Goose

~ February ~

Cast List

Group Captain and Mrs Blunt	*Retired airman and cosy wife*
Mrs Mayhew	*Schoolmistress on half-term*
Mr and Mrs Fisher	*Travellers: not tourists*
Mr Roberts	*Anxious accountant*
Hugh Young	*Mystery man*
Miss Chan	*Our guide*
And others	

All this took place in 1989, three months before the infamous massacre at Tianamen Square. China had woken from its Communist stupor and was soaring ahead economically; but from the tourists' point of view it was in transition; some things worked, some didn't; some people were friendly but nervous; others, sullen and unhelpful...........

Monday: Gatwick – Islamabad – Bejing

Group Captain Blunt is not happy. In fact he is gibbering with rage. We are flying with Pakistan Airlines and he has just been told that it is "dry." He is a small man. Dapper with thin grey hair, small neat moustache and a black patch over one eye. "I telephoned your company to check and I was assured that I would be able to get a drink. How is anyone expected to put up with eight hours, EIGHT hours, without one? Wouldn't have come on this trip if I'd known. Too late to cancel now." Storms off.

Poor chap; he's probably been up for hours worrying about going away and needs a drink to settle his nerves.

Mr Roberts asks how we are going to fill in the seven hour wait at Islamabad airport on our way home? He has left his wife behind and is obviously not used to coping on his own. He is wearing a Barbour over a dark suit and keeps patting the pockets to make sure he has his passport and ticket.

The Fishers, from Aberdeen, are wearing anoraks and walking boots, with knapsacks, their only luggage, slung across their backs. They would rather be travelling on their own.

I brave the Group Captain and suggest he buys a small bottle of whisky from the duty-free shop and keeps it well hidden. He can buy soda water on the aircraft. He cheers up immediately.

The plane is a jumbo jet. It takes off half an hour late and lands at Paris almost immediately. More passengers board, and there is a drama. Our party are sitting in their seats. "Sit tight for heaven's sake," I say. Arguments and shouting erupt, but we keep our heads down, and the unfortunate new arrivals are bundled off. It's three hours before we actually take off again.

Group Captain Blunt winks at me with his good eye and waves a bottle. At least he is happy. His wife looks plump and amiable. She is wearing a heavy sheepskin coat, which she is already regretting.

Hugh Young is agitated. He is concerned about our connection at Islamabad. "You are the tour manager – it's your responsibility to get us to Bejing. Go and speak to the pilot," he says rudely. He is rather an odd-fish – far younger than the rest of the party: shifty, doesn't look you in the eye. Perhaps he is nervous of flying. Best ignore him for the moment.

We arrive at Islamabad just in time for the connection to Bejing. Mad rush to check-in and we take off two hours later, arriving two hours late.

Bejing airport is a nightmare. Customs declaration forms and health forms to be filled in and signed.

Passports have to be collected and handed in, together with the group visa. Then luggage: half the party collect theirs and go through customs, but the carousel stops with a bump with no explanation.

I rush backwards and forwards through Customs, trying to find luggage, officials and guide, and placate increasingly irritated passengers.

At last the luggage is rounded up, and Miss Chan our guide, appears. She is young, small and neat, and speaks perfect English.

Off to the Bejing Toronto hotel – large and luxurious. Porters in uniform are hanging round the lounge, but there is no sign of any luggage. I suggest everyone goes to their rooms and I'll send it up when it comes, but they don't. They loiter around the front hall, looking conspicuously travel-worn compared with the smart Chinese coming and going through the lobby. The bags arrive an hour and a half later, having been round all the hotels in Bejing.

Some are too tired to come down to dinner, and those that do have great trouble with chopsticks, and ask for knives and forks. The Fishers don't like all this luxury. They wish they were staying in a proper Chinese hotel.

Tuesday: Bejing

Everybody is down on time, and there are no complaints about jet-lag. Breakfast of porridge, bacon, fried potatoes, scrambled eggs, tea and coffee. "Just like home," says Mrs Blunt. Cheerful staff and "Good morning: it's Tuesday" on the mats in the lift, so disorientated tourists know where they are.

It is a bright, cold day and everyone is pleased to be out in the fresh air. We are off to Tianamen Square, where Chairman Mao proclaimed the People's Republic in 1949. The roads are swarming with cyclists, all riding along at the same pace, jangling their bells, like a slow-moving swarm of bees.

The square is enormous. It can hold a million people, and even the pompous 1950s architecture, with a huge portrait of Mao hanging above the gate at one end, hasn't spoilt its imperial flavour. We stand around gawping at the size, and watch locals flying kites and tourists taking photographs, then stand in a long queue for Mao's mausoleum. When we reach it, we are rushed through by white-gloved officials telling us, through loudspeakers, to keep silent.

From there we walk through the gate to the Forbidden City. It is a series of gardens and halls built round large courtyards. Originally built over five hundred years ago, the scale of the whole place is overwhelming, and the yellow glazed roofs are dazzling against the blue sky.

It's a photographer's paradise and a tour leader's nightmare. Everyone shoots off in all directions and half an hour is spent rounding them up. They hadn't taken in that we are meeting at a different gate – even though we told them twice.

Lunch is at the Pavilion where we should be able to hear orioles. It's very noisy, and alas not an oriole to be heard for the roar of chattering diners.

Then we travel to the north of Peking to see the Summer Palace: a huge park, beautifully landscaped, with palaces, pavilions, halls and temples beside a frozen lake. The lake is entirely man-made and the earth from it was used to build Longevity Hill in the background. People are skating and sliding over the ice – like a Breugel painting come to life. There is a misty soft light with a pagoda rising out of hills in distance. At the edge of the shore there is a huge marble boat beached – looking like one of those college barges at Oxford. "Does it do pleasure trips?" asks Mrs Blunt. The Fishers nudge each other.

Everyone is happy. Couples are holding hands (always a good sign), chatting away about supermarkets, successful children, and, as always, the Royal Family. They are full of praise for the organisation of the tour. The Group Captain is smiling benignly, while Hugh Young and guide, Miss Chan, are engrossed in conversation well ahead of the group. They are speaking Mandarin to each other.

We walk uphill to the Azure Temple, passing between stalls selling fruit, nuts and eggs, boiled in tea, in enormous chipped enamel bowls. A good day and early bed.

Wednesday: Excursion from Bejing

Today is the Great Wall. Beautifully warm and sunny, with people regretting heavy winter coats and thermal underwear. On the way we visit the Ming Tombs – the burial ground of the Ming emperors, lying in a valley nestling under the mist-covered hills. We walk along the Spirit Way flanked by stone guardians – enormous warriors, Lord Mayors, town clerks and other majestic animals – and down ninety-one steps to the only tomb that has been excavated. It took 30,000 workers six years to complete it. "Makes you think," says Eileen Blunt.

The site is spoilt by souvenir stalls and photographers' kiosks. Clients are lent helmets or tiaras, and slip into place behind headless cut-outs of warriors or concubines. They look deliciously preposterous and take turns to photograph each other. No doubt their families and friends will enjoy the results.

On to the Great Wall. A highlight? No. Hundreds of tourist buses are belching out diesel fumes, and hundreds of tourists are spilling out of them doing much the same. Music blares through loudspeakers, postcard sellers make themselves a nuisance, stall-keepers sell tacky souvenirs.

The wall itself is much restored. It was built over 2,000 years ago and designed so that horsemen could ride six abreast between the crenellated walls. A world apart from the hordes of English school children playing football with empty Coca-Cola cans up and down the steps, in between the crowds.

Some of the group haggle for bargains in the souvenir shops, while the more energetic push through the mass of humanity and climb up to the tumbledown original wall. Away from the crowds it is romantic and empty and we get some impression of its length as we see it stretching, like a switchback, over the hills into the far distance.

We stop at a state-owned Friendship Shop on the way back, but it doesn't live up to its name. It's a large building with bright neon lights, practically empty, with surly staff selling overpriced goods. Much more fun to bargain with independent stall-holders.

We are having a Peking Duck banquet tonight – a must for all tourists, but some of the party, already fed up with Chinese food, decide to go to a European restaurant instead. Miss Chan gives us a "short briefing" (common phrase in China) on the preparation of Peking Duck. She mentions that the ducks are force-fed, so Margaret Mayhew, a wispy schoolmistress, decides she is a vegetarian and will just settle for the rice.

Thursday: Xian – Bejing

An early start and off to the airport for our flight to Xian and the Terracotta Army – the highlight of the tour. We are travelling with the local airline called, pompously, Civil Aviation Administration of China (CACC); but known informally as "China Airways Always Cancel." Let's hope not. Miss Chan is not coming with us and we have a local guide called Mr Wang.

I hand out boarding passes, but when we reach the plane it is a free-for-all and our party is scattered throughout the plane. The journey is meant to take just over an hour, but after two hours we start to get anxious. No sign of landing. Are we being hijacked? I am sitting at the front and turn round to see worried faces, so turn back quickly. An announcement comes over the intercom. Snow. There is no radar, so we can't land and must return to Bejing. No other information. On arrival we have to collect our luggage, but there is no sign of it. Mr Wang thinks it is a huge joke. We don't. The more able-bodied clients descend to the bowels of the airport and try to extricate our luggage from the piles of bags thrown on top of each other. Thank goodness for the large lurid labels which our travel company provide. After nearly two hours we have collected all of them and leave. Dinner is in a local restaurant and we spend the night in a modern hotel nearby, hoping for better luck tomorrow.

Friday: Xian – Bejing

Mr Roberts says his camera was stolen from the restaurant last night. He says he is very careful with possessions, so wouldn't have mislaid it. We go back to the airport via the restaurant, where a smiling manager hands over the camera found on the floor under the table.

The flight is advertised as taking off on time, and we get through the check-in, wait for three-quarters of an hour, and then are told that Xian airport is still closed. A decision will be made at lunch time. Everyone is fed up and there are no more compliments about the wonderful organisation. Our flight is called. Let's hope it's third time lucky.

Three clients have disappeared. I rush round looking for them, but they have walked straight through the ticket and visa checks unquestioned and are sitting in the best seats in the plane.

Fingers crossed, and we land safely at damp, dreary Xian airport.

Two thousand years ago this was the largest city in the world and the start of the silk route. This golden age ended about 1,000 AD when, after rebellion and anarchy, the city sank into provinciality and became a backwater. Much visited, mostly because it is the base for visiting the Terracotta Army, there is a lot to see, but we only have time to walk along the city walls and visit the Big Wild Goose pagoda – so called because of a legend; some meat-eating Buddhists were looking for food when a goose fell from the air in front of them with a broken wing. They took this as a sign that they should stop eating meat and built the pagoda in honour of the bird. Everyone climbs up the seven storeys – each one is meant to add another year to your life, but it's more like the opposite, judging from the huffing and puffing and panting and stopping.

We get back to our bus to find it surrounded by children selling painted wooden ducks. Clients buy armfuls of them. More and more bargaining and more and more ducks.

It's early dinner at the Xian hotel. We try to order Chinese wine without success, and end up with lukewarm Piat d'Or. It's better to stick to beer. We sit round after dinner drinking tea out of enormous mugs talking to another tour group. They tell us they went straight to see the Terracotta Army as soon as they arrived and found it closed. They have to get an early flight back to Bejing tomorrow morning. 8,000 miles for nothing.

Saturday: Xian

Today's the day. The site is eighteen miles to the east of Xian and on the way we stop for elevenses at the Hot Springs at Hua Quing. It was here that Chiang Kai Shek was captured by the communists in 1936, and it is now a much-visited beauty spot. We watch steam coming off ponds, out of buildings and through manhole covers. Mr Roberts, making the most of his reclaimed camera, takes photographs from all angles while the rest are impatient to get on.

Around 200 BC the Emperor Qin Shihuangdi, who built the Great Wall and burnt all the books (to make sure history would start with him), decided to build an underground empire so that he could go on enjoying glory and dignity after his death. He conscripted thousands of his subjects to construct his tomb – which lies, still unexcavated, under a huge mound nearby. The hundreds of pottery soldiers guarding it were found by accident thirty years ago when peasants came upon them while digging for water.

We arrive at what looks like an enormous aircraft hanger and are given a long, boring lecture on the Emperor. Lots of talk which we don't understand about "brown cherries," until someone realizes that they are bronze chariots. We walk through the hanger along raised wooden platforms, looking down on the army standing in trenches. It is extraordinarily moving, and rather eerie. The soldiers are massed in files, four abreast – more than six hundred of them, each with different features and expressions. Some of the party whizz through and make for souvenir shops, while others, fascinated by the army want to stand and stare, but are pushed along by the crowd pressing behind them. Mr Roberts starts taking photographs (strictly forbidden) and we are nearly thrown out.

We have a disappointing lunch and disgusting loos. Margaret Mayhew says they are not as bad as one she once went to in Wales.

Sunday: Xian – Bejing

The hotel forgets to give us our early call. Mrs Blunt says her cashmere jersey has come back matted and shrunk from the hotel's dry cleaners. Mr Roberts says someone has gone through his bags but nothing was taken. Mist and drizzle. Will our plane be able to take off? Some go to the museum and some to shops, while I stand outside and strain my ears for aircraft noise.

It's early lunch and off to the airport. The cloud gets lower, and everyone goes quiet. It's all right. Phew! We take off and land safely at Bejing, but there is no sign of Miss Chan. I telephone her office while the long-suffering clients wait patiently for a couple of hours until she appears. She was told that Xian airport was closed.

Back to the luxury of the Bejing Toronto which is too international for the Fishers, who go out to a local Chinese restaurant for dinner.

Monday: Bejing – Islamabad – London

Margaret Mayhew is furious. She had breakfast in bed and was made to pay. I have a word with reception. It was a misunderstanding, they say and refund her. "It's not the money; it's the principle of the thing," she says.

It is cold, bright, and windy. Our bags are packed and the bus is loaded. We have time to kill, so visit an antique market – a long street of shanty wooden shops, most of them closed, and those open all selling the same antiques. The wind is chilling, and ten minutes is more than enough, but we stay for two hours.

We stop for lunch on the way to the airport. Hugh Young says he is feeling ill and can't possibly fly back with us, so we stop at a police station to remove his name from the group visa and get an extended one for him. Time is running out and I telephone the airport: the plane is overbooked and they can't keep our seats. The police have disappeared into another building with the visa, and the clients sit anxiously in the bus. I sit fuming in the police station.

At last it is sorted out. We leave Hugh behind and get to the airport and through the check-in with minutes to spare. We sit and wait for an hour and a half. There is no explanation but suddenly a body on a stretcher, accompanied by six stalwart figures in white, is wheeled past the waiting crowd. Our plane has come from Japan and someone was taken ill. Off at last, with the same disgusting food and same rotten film.

We arrive at Islamabad at midnight, all set for the seven-hour wait at the airport that has been worrying Mr Roberts throughout the tour. How will we fill the time? The Group Captain suggests ten-pin bowling with our replicas of the Terracotta Army. The Fishers suggest dressing up in clothes we have bought, and acting charades. But another surprise awaits us – we are told to follow an official who leads us outside to a waiting bus. We drive through empty streets – "Are we being kidnapped?" asks Mr Roberts anxiously – and arrive at a small hotel where we are greeted by a huge doorman with a long orange beard, wearing flowing robes. He points to an eclipse of the moon which none of us has noticed, then gives us all mugs of green tea.

There aren't many rooms, so singles must double up. Margaret Mayhew is immediately back at reception saying there is a man in her bed. Everyone is grateful we aren't spending the night at the airport, so there are no complaints, even though the rooms are basic with no hot water, and lizards are running up and down the walls.

We are woken up by the manager. We've all overslept, but feel strangely refreshed. Was something slipped into the tea we wondered? Was it the eclipse? We bundle off to the airport and, surprise, surprise, the flight is delayed by two hours.

Mr Roberts reckons we have spent most of this holiday at airports or in aeroplanes. He will work out exactly how long and tell the travel company.

Jordan
Dead Sea Roles

~ March ~

Cast List

Dr and Mrs Mackay	*Ancient couple from Scotland*
Sir Philip and Lady White	*Industrialist from Lancashire*
Mrs Nash and Mrs Neel	*Farmers' wives*
Mr and Mrs Tallboy	*Assertive couple, unused to group travel*
Miss Baird	*From Edinburgh*
Mrs Bolton	*Widow from Hampstead*
And others	

Jordan is a brave country, with few natural assets and a desperate shortage of water. It is inhabited by two rather different people – the original Bedouin, hospitable and pious, in close touch with their rich cousins in Saudi Arabia, and Palestinians, largely religious, sophisticated and edgy. The country is held together by the monarchy – a benign autocracy with democratic trimmings.

Thursday: Heathrow – Amman

Dr and Mrs Mackay from Edinburgh are waiting at the airport long before time. Both are well over eighty, bent double and are carrying walking sticks and field glasses which are tangled up in the mackintoshes draped over their arms. She has faded red hair and a pale freckled complexion, and he has a beaky nose almost touching his chin, with just room for a crisp white moustache in between. At least they will be easy to spot.

Next to arrive are two younger women, farmers' wives from Somerset, thrilled to be on their own away from their chores and their husbands. They are old friends and never stop chattering. The rest of the group appear slowly, and at the last minute when I've almost given up, Mr and Mrs Tallboy, who have ignored the joining instructions, stroll confidently up to the check-in desk. I know their type – they don't want to be associated with a group and will show their independence by always being late.

We have an uneventful flight to Amman, and on arrival everyone walks straight past the agent holding up a large sign with the name of our group on it and disappears into the loo or to the money changers.

The luggage comes through quickly, but there is no sign of the Mackays' walking sticks and other tours sweep past us. The sticks appear one by one and we go through a final frisk before meeting our guide, Suleyman. Not so fast. Dr Mackay is the last to come through and the officials don't like the look of his field glasses. He is sent back through Customs and the military police are summoned to examine his bags. The airport is now deserted and the rest of our party are sitting disconsolately in the bus outside the building. I am about to send them off without him, when he hobbles into sight holding us up even further by apologising to everyone as he makes his way to the back of the bus. We go straight to our hotel which is a modern building in the "hotel" area of Amman, and everyone has to hang around for a welcome drink they don't want. Bed at 3.30am.

Friday: Amman

Nowadays groups stay in bland, modern hotels with identical rooms. Old fashioned hotels with charm can cause problems because the rooms vary in size, comfort and view. And of course single women, who have to pay a supplement anyway, are understandably furious if given a shoe-box above the kitchen. This hotel is a classic example of the modern type and inside we could be at any similar hotel in the world. Outside the khamseen – a warm wind from the desert – is blowing, and the sky looks misty, not from cloud, but from sand and dust swirling around.

The group appears in an extraordinary selection of head gear: straw hats, head scarves, cricket cap (too small) and a couple of parasols. Sir Philip White, large, northern and important, is sporting a baseball cap with "Warrington FC" embroidered on the peak. His wife, nearly as large with dyed blonde hair, wears enormous sunglasses hiding almost none of her moon-shaped face, and her holiday clothes are just a little too tight for her.

Nash and Neel, egging each other on, say they must have the front seats otherwise they will "throw up." So will Mrs Bolton, from a distance bespectacled and fuzzy, like a rather shy moth, but closer up the look in her eye contradicts this assumption. She gets the front seats to herself.

We set off northwards for the Roman city of Jerash, a fine city in its day and still an imposing site, with its enormous oval forum, and still-standing colonnade of Corinthian pillars.

Gerasa, as it was originally known, built up its enormous wealth over two centuries through trading, iron-ore mining, and farming in the fertile country surrounding it. It reached its peak in the third century. The development of sea-trade, and the demise of caravans passing through, pushed the city into a slow decline. It was more or less deserted for several hundred years and not until excavations began in the 1870s was its importance recognised.

The guide book suggests three hours to see everything, but after an hour we are still under the imposing Triumphal

Arch at the entrance to the city. Suleyman talks and talks. He is a young man, well-built and well-educated and wants to show off his knowledge by showing us every stone of every building. It is boiling hot, and I keep looking at my watch and try and egg him on without success.

Dr Mackay's shoe fall to bits. Has he taken the words of the psalm literally? "Over Edom will I cast out my shoe." I borrow two large plastic bags from a stall-holder and tie up his feet in them: not surprisingly he makes slow progress.

Everyone is getting restless and at last we stop for lunch at a Lebanese restaurant under a eucalyptus tree. Then on to the ancient theatre where we are all made to march on to the stage together, in time to the Grand March from *Aida*, played on strange bagpipes and drums, followed by the *Skye Boat Song* – no doubt for the Edinburgh lot.

Who is going to declaim? Nobody volunteers, until little Connie Baird, a nervous, skinny woman, perhaps encouraged by Speed Bonnie Boat, stands up and, self-consciously twirling her parasol above her head, says "To be or not to be, that is the question." She then sits down quickly.

We get back to the hotel, only having seen half of what was intended, with a few minutes to change before going out to dinner.

I've told the office in London so many times that we shouldn't go out to dinner the first night, but here we are setting out for a half-hour drive to a restaurant in the suburbs; an old farm converted into a tourist attraction complete with a craft centre. Just what we need after a long day, but the food is good and there is plenty of wine so everyone bucks up.

Mrs Tallboy points to photographs of the Jordanian Royal Family round the wall and tells us that her sister was at school with Princess Alia. We aim to leave by 10pm, but are delayed by some people who start shopping and going to the loo.

We move off slowly. Something is wrong and the driver can't get out of second gear. Suleyman looks anxious and gets on his mobile. "No problem," he keeps saying when there is obviously a big problem as we are crawling along at ten miles an hour.

I tell everyone cheerfully that you need three qualities to survive a group holiday – patience, flexibility and a sense of humour. It goes down like a lead balloon. Mr Tallboy, Napoleonic stockbroker, has a grand sense of humour failure. He is furious. "Why don't we get taxis?" (There aren't any). Mrs Mackay, who is ancient but loud and screechy, screams "Why can't you provide a decent bus?" Lady White, (Empress of the North) says "We are very angry," and Nash and Neel just get the giggles. Suleyman is flustered: but won't lose face. "We will get this bus mended by tomorrow," he says. "We want a new bus," they shout, "not a mended one." We creep along, the atmosphere loaded, and eventually reach the outskirts of Amman at midnight. Suleyman flags down taxis and we quickly reach the hotel.

Saturday: Amman – Wadi Rum – Petra

I didn't sleep a wink worrying about the wretched bus. Would they get a new one in time or will they repair the old one? I needn't have worried because as I stand anxiously outside the hotel the driver turns up early with a new bus and everyone is on time except the Tallboys who, as I thought, have already made it clear that they are on holiday and won't be hurried. Nash and Neel, red-faced and jolly, but not averse to a bit of competition, throw themselves into the front seats giggling, while Mrs Bolton, knowing she is beaten and looking like a thundercloud, retreats.

A tourist policeman joins us. "He is here to keep an eye on us," says Suleyman. Our "protector" stretches out on the back seat and falls asleep.

We travel down the King's Highway – an ancient road of great significance. It was used by Christian pilgrims going to Mount Nebo, Muslim pilgrims going to Mecca, and Nabateans going to and fro to Petra. It is now a good, fast road, but the journey takes longer than scheduled on account of frequent stops for visits to gift shops.

Wadi Rum is gaunt and beautiful: red sand, red-brown mountains rising vertically out of the desert, shaped like vast, craggy tea-cosies. The khamseen is still blowing, so the sharp peaks known as the "Seven Pillars of Wisdom" stand up eerily out of the blowing sand.

We have a simple lunch in a rest house, then pile into battered old jeeps for an exhilarating ride through the desert, stopping a couple of times to look at T.E.

Lawrence's favourite watering place and a gorge with ancient graffiti scrawled on the rock.

It is getting late and we don't reach our hotel in Petra until after 7pm, sand-swept and tired, ready for hot baths and large drinks.

But there aren't enough rooms to go round. Mrs Bolton and Miss Baird will have to share, and two couples will have to go down the road to an annexe. Mrs Bolton refuses point-blank, saying she wouldn't even share a room with her daughter, let alone a stranger. Poor little Connie Baird says nothing, and everyone else starts complaining except Nash and Neel.

I find the manager, and plead with him to find some more rooms. A group from Japan has been delayed, so we can have their rooms tonight. And tomorrow? "Tomorrow is another day."

What on earth am I doing in this job?

This is a large, newly-built hotel, with a grand restaurant, beautifully decorated in Middle Eastern style. Dr and Mrs Mackay insist on sitting next to each other at every meal. They have been married for ever and have long since run out of conversation and sit in silence which is rather a damper for their neighbours. There is a good service here and excellent food, and Mr Tallboy is going to order more wine until he sees the price.

Sunday: Petra

So now for Petra – one of the most magical places in the world. It was built by the Nabataeans – an Arab tribe who found an ideal solution to the problem of living comfortably in a rough world.

When, in 586 BC the Babylonians destroyed Jerusalem and carried off the Israelites, they left a vacuum. The Edomites of the desert moved in leaving their old territory vacant. So the Nabataens took over, and found themselves astride one of the main trade routes from Asia to the Mediterranean. They set themselves up as brigands evolving seamlessly into customs officers, collecting money from every caravan that passed. Best of all, they were in a gap between Egypt and Syria where neither state could easily get at them, protected as they were by miles of desert. Making Petra their capital, they soon became rich and stayed rich. Even when they were finally absorbed into the Roman Empire, they went on doing what they did best, making money.

But alas – the trade winds were discovered, big ships were built and sea-born traffic by-passed them.

By the end of Roman times they were poor, and by the Middle Ages Petra was deserted and lost from memory, and wasn't heard of again till the Swiss explorer Jean Louis Burckhardt discovered it in 1812.

The wind has dropped and the sky is clear. We have agreed to start at 8am. Not difficult as our hotel is two minutes' walk from the site, but there is much time-wasting at the Visitor Centre buying guide-books and postcards and going back to the hotel for cardigans or more cash.

You get to Petra through the Siq – a narrow canyon almost meeting overhead, with red walls hundreds of feet high. At the end you are suddenly faced with the Treasury – a palace carved out of rock, glowing in sunlight, protected by its position from sand and wind, and fresh and crisp as the day it was built.

Beyond, where the canyon widens into a bowl, is the city itself. What makes the sight so astonishing is the colour of the rock: as Edward Lear's cook described it – "Master, we have come into a world of chocolate, ham, curry powder and salmon."

Such beauty should dwarf squalid human concerns, but the squalid humans are around in crowds. There are carriages lined up below the Visitor Centre and you can ride down the Siq in them if you can't manage the walk. I persuade Dr MacLean – shoes now mended with string and super-glue – to hitch a lift.

Everybody wants to get moving, but Suleyman spends ages giving an unwanted history lesson.

By the time we reach the Siq itself, it is heaving with tourists. A large party of Germans all wearing identical red baseball caps, swarm into the Treasury and start singing hymns. Our gang emerges behind them, silent for once, over-whelmed by the drama of the gorge with its layers of coloured rock.

We move slowly down into the huge open site, stopping at a stall where bedouin children with runny noses smeared with sand, are selling trays of shards, coins and coloured rock. There are miniature Johnnie Walker bottles filled with striped sand – just like Alum Bay in the Isle of Wight, except that here you can have your name written on the outside in Arabic.

The Tallboys, impatient to see everything, branch off and climb up to the High Place where they find an Australian girl with a rucksack, fast asleep on the sacrificial altar. They are not surprised to find us still at the same stall when they come down half an hour later.

We have lunch in a huge dark canteen at the far end of the site. A real scrum. A buffet with masses of choice and for pudding rose-red jelly – half as old as time?

The Germans are holding a communion service in the Roman theatre so we can't go there. "Typically selfish," says Mrs Bolton. We climb the hill to the monastery of El Deir, in the baking heat. Some walk and some ride donkeys – terrifying as the donkeys have to walk up steep steps (worse still coming down). Sir Philip is taking it slowly, while describing the complications of his recent triple-heart by-pass operation. He should be in a wheel-chair says his wife. At the top we have mint tea in a bedouin tent, looking across the city to the mountains beyond.

By this time most tourists have left and we walk back along the Colonnade Street enjoying the quiet in the soft, evening light.

Miraculously the hotel has found us all rooms and we go on to the roof to watch the sunset. All in a good mood. Some stay in the hotel and have an excellent dinner while the rest of us, feeling more adventurous, go with Suleyman to a dingy local restaurant run by friends of his.

It is within walking distance of the hotel, so on the way we stop at a very expensive handicraft market and Suleyman hovers around us while we don't buy. No commission for him.

Monday: Petra – Amman

"And Moses went up from the plains of Moab unto the mountain of Nebo."

A full day ahead, so an early start. No sign of the Tallboys and I find them in the dining room eating boiled eggs. "We'll come when we're ready.' Everyone sits fuming on the bus, and the late-comers arrive with no apologies.

A long drive, and a long stop at a shop selling products from the Dead Sea. The management would like to give me a present. I choose a bar of mud soap, wondering what they offered Suleyman, as the longer we stay the more the clients buy. Mrs Bolton decides she wants coffee just as we are leaving.

It is mid-afternoon when we reach our hotel for lunch. A beautiful site with well-kept gardens stretching down to the sea. "Why aren't we staying here?" they all ask. Good question.

Suleyman says we must leave promptly as Mount Nebo closes at 5pm. Sir Philip says we must skip Mount Nebo and stay longer here, so does Mrs Mackay. "Surely nobody wants to go to Mount Nebo when they could stay in this lovely place? We must take a vote on it." "No," I say. "You must never leave something out that is written in the itinerary, because you can bet your bottom dollar it is the one place somebody has come especially to see." They are not pleased.

They rush through lunch and go down to the sea. "Be very careful," says Suleyman. "Don't, whatever you do, get water in your eyes, and take off your gold jewellery because the salt will turn it black." Lady White is covered in jewels and takes some time to remove it all from ears, fingers, wrists and neck, and hands it to me for safe-keeping.

I sit indoors and chat up Suleyman who is in a sulk. Tour leaders must never fall out with the guide and most are easy to get on with, but in Arab countries they don't like taking instructions from women. They are well-educated and want to hand out every bit of knowledge that they know. Suelyman is a prize example.

Nash and Neel come bursting in. Sir Philip has turned turtle in the Dead Sea, has swallowed water and is in a bad way. We rush down to the medical room where he is gasping for breath. His face is bright red, burning with the salt, eyes streaming. "We told him not to go in," they say. "But he did, and immediately flipped over." A life-guard dived in after him and hauled him out.

After a while he gets his breath back and looks better, but we must take him to the nearest hospital to be checked and x-rayed. No hope of getting to Mount Nebo now.

A tense, long bus journey through the narrow streets of the nearest town as nobody seems to know where the hospital is. When we do find it, Sir Philip and I are dropped off and Suleyman takes the others to see a church with a map of the Holy Land in ancient mosaics.

No waiting in the hospital. X-ray at once. Our charming doctor speaks fluent English and says this is a very dispiriting place to work. We are the first Europeans he has seen here in two years. The x-ray is fine, and there is no water in his lungs but Sir Philip is put on a ventilator, and a saline drip to refresh his blood. Curious nurses and patients and patients' families crowd round his bed to watch.

Suleyman rushes in. The church was closed and we must go immediately as he has left the others at a craft centre. Snatches away the ventilator and drip, and hauls confused Sir Philip off the bed and into a waiting taxi. The rest of the party are standing impatiently outside the craft centre. We head straight back to Amman, not stopping on the way. The Tourist policeman finally wakes up and Suleyman asks for a Big Hand because he has looked after us so well.

Back at the hotel I check arrangements for our special last-night dinner. None of the restaurants in the hotel have our booking, but I am finally directed downstairs to the ballroom. Three huge round tables in an empty soulless, bare room. Third-rate dinner. Sir Philip, completely recovered, is the life and soul of the party. Wine flows and flows, but when the waiter asks me to sign bill, I notice that he has charged extra for all these bottles.

Tuesday: Amman – Heathrow

Early breakfast in subterranean ballroom with everyone feeling grumpy. Mrs Mackay wants "cooked breakfast," but it's not available down here. Mrs Tallboy is furious. Mount Nebo was the only reason they had come on this trip and she will get her money back from the tour company. Mrs Bolton will only travel with this company again if she can be guaranteed a front seat on the bus. No sign of Suleyman, but an official from his office arrives to take us to the airport, and sweeps us effortlessly through various controls and check-ins. I ask him to book me a seat as far as possible from the rest to the party.

On our return several of the party wrote to complain about the ineffectual tour manager. The tour company responded by sending everyone a generous cheque for missing Mount Nebo. Two people write and thank.

Waterloo
A Damn Close-Run Thing

~ April ~

Cast List

Brigadier Christopher Collins	*Our lecturer: an authority on Waterloo*
Colonel and Mrs Chamberlain	*Gentle husband with overbearing wife*
Major Cramp	*Enjoyer from Wiltshire – came to Leningrad in January*
Mr and Mrs Everard	*Ancient guardsman with younger wife*
Lady Southwood	*Scatty widow*
Captain Clifton-Jones	*Young and handsome*
Sir Brian Weston	*Retired judge*
And others	

Waterloo – the battle still rages in the mind-set of the French and English, as any match at Twickenham will demonstrate. Napoleonic flair throws in the Old Guard; British grit keeps them out. But the British too have their Old Guard – old men from a nobler age, who fought bravely in the wars, never cheated, never doubted and never gave in. Or if they ever had, their wives would still be there to give the enemy hell. On this tour they were out in force.

Friday: London – Brussels

We are going to Brussels by Eurostar. It should be a piece of cake, with no queues for check-in, passport control or security. No drinking coffee at overpriced cafeterias and no screens saying "Delayed. Wait in Hall."

Today the Terminal at Waterloo is swarming with the usual holiday riff-raff and their clutter – anoraks, trainers, knapsacks, mobile phones and personal stereos. Out of this crowded scene appear trolleys, piled high with suitcases – wheeled very, very slowly by their owners, just peeping over the top of the pile. Tweed coats, Barbours, guards' ties, flat caps, polished shoes, shooting sticks, hearing aids and loud voices.

The holiday riff-raff look on amazed. Everyone seems to know everyone else or everyone else's relations, and the words "Small World" are ringing round the concourse.

Our lecturer, Brigadier Collins is the centre of attention. He is a good-looking, elderly man, and every bit the retired soldier, with a straight back, straight parting through thin grey hair, and straight nose to match. He has taken tours to Waterloo for years and has a loyal following. He is wearing a navy-blue blazer with enormous brass buttons, grey flannels, guards' tie and a panama hat. He looks immaculate.

Everyone has arrived except for the Everards and I try and persuade them all to go through the ticket barrier, but they are so happy chatting that they are reluctant to move until the last minute. They have all been worrying about arriving in time, but now they are here they have completely given up thinking for themselves. Some can't manage the ticket machine – you put your ticket in at the bottom and take it out at the top, but Major Cramp's ticket gets completely mangled and the entire queue is held up, until he is given a new one.

A taxi draws up and a large bundle of ginger corduroy extricates itself. Mr Everard. He shuffles along slowly, grunting and puffing. He has fading gingerish hair that matches his corduroy suit, and watery eyes look bewildered by the scene in front of him. His much younger pale-faced wife looks on nervously as he is pushed through the barrier by officials – thus bypassing the frisking machines.

We take the escalator up to the platform and I fuss around to make sure everyone is aboard our train.

The train on the adjacent platform is about to leave for Paris and I suddenly catch sight of Lady Southwood looking out of a window. I rush over, haul her and her luggage off and into our train with seconds to spare.

Some of the party are travelling first-class and are tucking into hearty breakfasts washed down by champagne, while others, like children on a school trip, are starting on lunch. It has been provided by one of the London military clubs: thick sandwiches made with white bread, pork pies and a small bottle of red wine. "Why weren't we given a choice of red or white?" asks Mrs Chamberlain. She is a formidable woman whose nose nearly touches her chin, with darting small eyes looking for trouble. Her tightly permed curls are kept in place with frequent doses of hair spray. Her husband is rather quiet, and like all men with bossy wives, pretends not to hear.

There is a long delay in the tunnel, so our train is late. It is very hot in the carriages and the men have taken their coats off. All are wearing braces – some red, some yellow. Major Cramp's have union jacks stretched up and down them. He has left his wife at home in Wiltshire and has come to enjoy himself, starting off with a bottle of champagne which he shares with Captain Clifton-Jones. After we leave Lille he realises that someone has left the train with his suitcase, leaving an almost identical one behind. Nothing can be done at this stage.

Our guide Etienne is waiting for us at the barrier in Brussels, and everyone wants the loo. It needs a 25 cent coin and no one has got one, so it all takes ages. Why on earth didn't they go on the train?

Brigadier Collins and I go to report the lost luggage, then take the underground to the Hotel Metropole, while Etienne takes the clients on a bus tour of Brussels.

I check the bedrooms and rush out to inspect the restaurant for dinner, while the Brigadier spends the afternoon in conference with the hotel technicians, trying to work the projector for his talk and slide show of Waterloo this evening. The projector won't work, so the technicians produce another one, which doesn't work either, but third time lucky, although the slides will have to be put in by hand. "These slides are too old for modern projectors," says the electrician. Some of them drop down inside and clog up the works, which doesn't augur well for the talk later on.

The bus party arrives at the hotel with the luggage, but the old and authentic art-nouveau lift isn't working. "It had to be modernized for 'Health and Safety'," says the concierge. "It worked perfectly for a hundred years, but now it's always breaking down." The modern lift along the passage only takes two people at a time, so it takes ages for everyone to get up to their rooms.

Meanwhile Mr Everard has disappeared. He had a stroke four years ago and is very forgetful. He had agreed to meet wife at a café, but an hour later there is still no sign of him. He eventually appears, having been waiting at the wrong café.

Everyone is on time – with drinks of course – for the Brigadier's talk. I stand at the ready, poised to press the button for the slides to move on, but the projector has a mind of its own and clicks on to the next slide by itself, so when the Brigadier turns round to point with his umbrella, at say, a battlefield scene, he finds he is actually pointing at Napoleon's head or Wellington's horse.

Stimulated by this rather hilarious entertainment and fortified by drinks, we set out on foot for dinner at a restaurant near La Grande Place.

We walk through this huge open space, originally a market, surrounded by guildhalls belonging to merchants – each one different from the one next to it and with façades decorated with statues and carvings.

Everyone looks longingly at the cheerful-looking tourist rip-off restaurants lining the streets leading off the Grande Place. There are tables outside under calor gas heaters, with red and white checked tablecloths and a happy buzz of conversation.

Captain Clifton-Jones (Master of Foxhounds) spots one of his hunt followers. "Small world," they both say. After our excellent dinner in a rather modest-looking restaurant, some go back to the hotel and others stay out to look for further entertainment. No sign of Major Cramp's bag and a sleepless night for me worrying about it.

Saturday: Brussels – Waterloo

Breakfast is in the old ball-room in the basement. They all tuck into a "Full English" and read the Financial Times. Major Cramp mentions that his bag turned up last night. I wish he'd told me then.

Everyone assembles in the lobby with the Everards last to appear, having missed breakfast as they forgot to put their clock forward. The Brigadier says Wellington didn't allow his troops breakfast before going into battle.

Most are wearing country clothes. Captain Clifton-Jones looks ready for a day's shooting in knee breeches and stockings with knitted garters. The Brigadier looks handsome in a tweed suit, waistcoat and still the guards' tie, but Sir Brian lowers the tone in a navy blue suit and black shoes, while Colonel Chamberlain's green husky, with strips of peeling sticking plaster all over it, is shown up by his wife's immaculate red Jaeger coat and silk headscarf.

We are just about to board the bus when the hall porter dashes up with lost property – one camera, one banana, one shooting stick.

The battlefield is twelve miles south of Brussels and we approach it through the Foret de Soignes – miles of beech woods looking pale and elegant in the early Spring light.

The most prominent feature of the battlefield is Lion Hill – a huge man-made mound with the statue of a Lion on top, raised as a Netherlands' memorial in the 1820s. It dominates the countryside – still mostly open farmland, as it was then, but the removing of vast amounts of earth has changed the subtle contours of the land and when Wellington returned to the site a few years later he complained that they had ruined his battlefield.

We drive to various key points and hop on and off the coach. The Brigadier gives a short talk at each stop. He has a loud, clear voice and most listen intently, although some of the older, deafer men wander off and discuss tactics among themselves.

The first stop is Quatre Bras where we inspect a memorial to the British – recently unveiled by the present Duke of Wellington. Everyone points proudly to his regiment. Grenadiers, Green Jackets. Mr Smith, who has confessed to me that he doesn't feel quite at home in this upper-class party, feels more confident when he sees that his Essex regiment was there too.

Then to La Belle Alliance, where the British could see the French and hear their drums. And afterwards, La Haie Sainte – held by the German Legion – Hanoverian exiles in British service, and Thomas Picton's memorial where he shouted "Charge" and was shot dead from his horse a moment later. The hedges, where his Scottish regiments burst through, are no longer there, and the ditch is now lined with Japanese knotweed – sparking off a gardening discussion among our country folk.

Time for a pause. We park at the bottom of Lion Hill and the Brigadier and I go off to check the restaurant for lunch. "Time spent in reconnaissance is seldom wasted," he says and suggests the others climb up the steps to the top of Lion Hill or go and visit the museum next door.

Neither. They make a bee-line for the nearest café and sit drinking brandy and coffee until we return. We leave them to it and go and look at a panorama of the battle housed in a rotunda built to commemorate the centenary: a huge scene of a French cavalry charge with Wellington nowhere to be seen – certainly nowhere very obvious. We go to the shop to buy postcards where there are plenty of Napoleon in different poses, the Prince of Orange and

Blucher with his soup-strainer moustache, but not one of Our Hero.

We round up the troops and set off for a short ride to Hougoumont where we walk up a lane to a peaceful collection of ancient farm buildings. It is hard to imagine the bloody battle that was fought here. The chateau at the side of the farmyard was burnt to the ground, but the chapel, farmhouse and barns remain.

We stand by the open gateway where the Brigadier describes the strategic importance of the farm in the surrounding countryside. There used to be a solid wooden gate here, and on the closing of this against the French army, Wellington said afterwards, the success of the battle depended. A place of pride for the Brigadier and other Coldstreamers in the party, because it was their regiment, along with the Scots Guards, who defended it.

The Brigadier is old friends with the farmer and his wife, and they show us round their house and then the inside of the chapel. We look at a wooden crucifix, with the feet of Christ showing scorch marks from the flames that burnt much of the inside of the building.

We wander round the grounds taking photographs or discussing the importance of the battle. None of the usual package tour chat about grandchildren and cruises and the Royal Family. Mr Everard is deep in a 1906 Baedeker.

Lunch is at the 1815 restaurant where wine is provided and more bottles are ordered. The owner appears and makes a short speech telling us it was Blucher who won the Battle of Waterloo. We are too polite to argue. Beside the restaurant large fields of tulips are being harvested. Colonel Chamberlain, touchingly, buys a huge bunch for his wife, who isn't pleased at having to carry it around with her.

Last stop is at Mercer's Ridge – the final battle of the day – so called because a Captain Mercer placed his guns behind a long bank so that they were almost at ground level and thus hidden from the French. Mr Everard needs a pee and nowadays there is no hiding place, so he goes against side of the coach. Everyone tactfully looks the other way.

On the way back we stop briefly at the Wellington Museum, formerly a coaching inn and Wellington's headquarters for the battle. There are souvenirs, weaponry and illuminated panels showing the progress of the battle through the day.

Our driver is in a state. A grey nylon antimacassar has gone missing from one of the seats. Would we all check our bags to see whether we have taken it?

Back at the Metropole we drink tea or something stronger in the delightful art-nouveau brasserie, packed with locals and thick with cigarette smoke. After that it's a free evening. Lady Southwood wants to take Major Cramp for a Vietnamese dinner, some want fish while others make bee-line to the touristy rip-offs we passed on the first night. Everyone has paired up, so I cross the road to the cinema opposite, and go to see Four Weddings and a Funeral – much enjoyed by the Belgian audience.

Sunday: Brussels – Bruges – London

We are going to spend today at Bruges before driving back to Brussels to catch the Eurostar. Etienne arrives punctually, but there is no sign of a coach. The clients hang around on the pavement with their luggage wishing they hadn't had to get up so early. The coach arrives, and the hall porter appears with lost property: one umbrella, one cap, one shooting-stick.

Colonel Chamberlain has lost his train tickets. Mrs Chamberlain is panicking, so they sit at the back of the coach and go through their bags, scattering papers everywhere, and of course the tickets turn up. Mrs C. realises she has left her hair-dryer in the hotel, but it's too late to go back.

It is sunny when we leave Brussels and raining when we get to Bruges, so the driver has to get the luggage out of the bus and everyone delves into their bags to get warmer clothes, umbrellas and waterproofs.

Most are wearing Barbours, but Lady Southwood looks slightly out of place in a white plastic mackintosh with "Wimbledon 1992" printed in green and purple on the back. We walk through the grounds of a nunnery with a sign saying "Silence Please" – unnoticed by our group who chatter loudly.

The streets are crowded with tourists and cars, and clients keep falling off pavements or darting into shops. Some go and see the Michelangelo in the Cathedral, and others just sit outside or go shopping.

There is so much to see in Bruges but we have very little time and a boat trip along the canals has been prearranged, with a loudspeaker commentary in English. It is freezing cold and wet, with occasional views of houses – above, below and through umbrellas. We welcome lunch in a cosy restaurant, where one free drink is included, but unfortunately it's coffee, not alcohol.

Mrs Chamberlain suggests we leave promptly so we can visit Ghent on our way back to Brussels. Everyone assembles on time except the Chamberlains who emerge slowly from a chocolate shop: no time to visit Ghent. In fact there is no time to waste, but the coach is stopped by police on the motorway. Papers, first-aid kit, tyres and seat-belts are all inspected and it takes ages. I look at my watch. Traffic is heavy in Brussels, and when we arrive at the station there are no trolleys, no staff and no information. The Eurostar terminal still hasn't been completed, and the whole station is a nightmare – but luckily I know it well. "Follow me," I say sharply. Up escalators, down escalators, along passages and across the concourse through the ticket barrier and on to the train which leaves straight away.

Why did I think this would be more restful than flying?

Antalya and Istanbul
See-saw

~ May ~

Cast List

Mr and Mrs Grey	*"Wooden Leg"*
Mr & Mrs Stewart Taylor	*"Fishing Socks"*
Mr Innes	*Retired classics master*
Mr and Mrs Scott	*From Orpington*
Mrs Gloria Gunn	*Their friend*
Lord and Lady Palmer	*Elderly peer and wife (who came to Leningrad in January)*

And others

Five hundred years ago, the Turks ruled the Balkans and the whole Middle East, and were threatening Rome and Vienna. A hundred years ago they were still a great power: at its peak the Ottoman empire was as wide as the British and lasted a great deal longer. To us it seems both romantic and sinister – a world of Sultans and odalisques, Byronic heroes and bashi bazouks, but in its glory days it must have seemed the greatest and most progressive power in the world. The First World War ended it, and Turkey became what it had never been – a country on its own. It was lucky in its leader: the great general Mustapha Kemal Ataturk, who had beaten the allies at Gallipoli, took control and founded the modern republic – secular, Europe-minded, and (thanks to a bit of ethnic cleansing) all Turkish – except for the Kurds in the South East of the country, who remain restless.

The Turks got where they are by replacing the old Byzantine Empire. Its capital, Constantinople, was captured in 1453 by Sultan Mehmet II The Conqueror. Suleyman The Magnificent, a contemporary of Henry VIII, pushed the empire to its widest limits, while his son, Selim the Sot, began the slow decline. Most of the sites we visited on this tour were full of reminders of their Byzantine past, and before that of the Roman and Greek empires that went before.

Saturday: Heathrow – Istanbul

However early I arrive at an airport someone is there before me, and some, like the Palmers look tense and disorientated. By the time they have got the dogs to kennels, stopped the newspapers, locked up the house and left home at the crack of dawn having not slept a wink, and however much they've been looking forward to it, the last thing they want is to go on holiday.

I am slightly alarmed by Gloria Gunn's cowboy outfit (suede skirt and waistcoat with tassels, leather boots and a huge-brimmed hat over long grey hair), but otherwise nothing out of the ordinary.

At Istanbul, we side-step the queues at immigration and go through the "Turkish Nationals Only" booth. Nobody questions us.

We meet our guide Sule who is waiting with the bus. She is smiling, tall with dark hair and olive skin, but what is striking about her are her green eyes – rather unusual for a Turk.

Our hotel is right in the centre of the old city – almost underneath the Blue Mosque and within walking distance of all the main sites.

Mrs Scott, a big bossy woman with a jutting out chin, immediately wants to change her room – it is much too small. The hotel manager says it is one of the largest. Mr Scott, fat and jolly, backs away – used to these situations and is not going to get involved.

It's the usual Welcome Drinks in the bar, but there is slight confusion because another group identical to ours is staying here. Same clothes, same voices, same friends, same drinks, same Small World. Nobody is sure which group they belong to. Mr Stewart Taylor recognises an old army friend called Waddles and I see an overweight old school friend called Twiggy.

Our dreary dinner in a basement dining room is lamb stew with frozen brussels sprouts and overcooked carrots, but everyone is chatting so hard they don't notice. Gloria Gunn and Sheila Scott are old friends and talk exclusively to each other ignoring neighbours. Mr Stewart Taylor, a farmer from Gloucestershire, has a red face, loud laugh and a schoolboy sense of humour which embarrasses his quiet wife. Mr Grey – retired engineer from Nottingham – and wife are already on their third holiday, or break as they call it, this year.

Sunday: Istanbul

Breakfast is on the roof terrace. It's rather chilly, but the view over mosques and houses to the Sea of Marmara makes up for it. The sea is alive with shipping: tankers, fishing boats, cruise ships, ferries. "A Sight so Touching in its Majesty" (Mr Innes recites Wordsworth). He is a retired schoolmaster, wearing a thin corduroy jacket: thin sandy hair, thin face and thin nose. He calls Istanbul "Constantinople," and fills in what the guide leaves out.

We go by coach to the Dolmabahce Palace, crossing the Golden Horn by the Galatea bridge. The palace was built on the banks of the Bosphorus in the middle of the nineteenth century as an over-the-top Ottoman-European fantasy. The Empire may have been in decline, but the Sultan wanted the world to see that Turkey still had a bit of style.

Unfortunately we don't see it. It is a national holiday and the government has given Turks a free pass into all public buildings. The queue for entrance stretches for miles.

We abandon the visit and go to the Chora church instead. Chora means "in the country," but the church has long since been engulfed in urban sprawl and the present church, is now a museum. It is packed with tourists and locals, but we manage to squeeze in and catch glimpses of the frescoes and mosaics – white-washed over during four centuries of Ottoman rule, and so preserved in perfect condition.

Then on to see a mosque built for Suleyman the Magnificent – the Suleymaniye Mosque. There is maximum palaver at the entrance. Lady Palmer – tall, elegant and beautifully dressed – is reluctant to take off her shoes because she might get verrucas. Gloria is worried that someone might steal her Size 9 riding boots. Mr Stewart Taylor has had polio and is unable to take his shoes off, but has brought his fishing socks which he pulls on over the top. Mr Grey has a wooden leg which is more of a problem but, as in Jordan, I get two plastic bags, one black and one white, from a stallholder outside the mosque, and he steps into these which we tie up with string. Problem solved.

Sinan was the architect for Suleyman in the golden age of the Ottoman Empire and this mosque is the grandest and most visited of Sinan's works: the inside is cool and calm, with little decoration except for some Isnik tiles and some gorgeous stained glass windows.

Next stop: Topkapi Palace – built by Sultan Mehmet II, after he had sacked Constantinople. The Imperial family lived here until 1853 when they moved to the Dolmabahce, and it became a state museum in 1924.

It is a huge site and it can't possibly be crowded; but it is. There are queues for everything. Our party particularly wants to visit the harem and court of the concubines, but so does the rest of Turkey. The Imperial treasury, costume collection, palace kitchens – they are all packed. We wander through disconsolately, everyone except Mr Innes, keeping close together for fear of getting lost. A keen scholar determined to see everything, he keeps darting off and the others start complaining.

We walk through the gardens and arrive at a terrace-restaurant with a beautiful view over the Bosphorus. Everyone cheers up until we are ushered into a small room for lunch, so dark and crowded that we can't see what we are eating – let alone the view. Sheila Scott pulls two quarter bottles of champagne out of her bag. "Never travel without these," she says.

"Sultan Selim the Sot drowned in his bath after drinking too much champagne," reads Fishing Socks from his guide book. "Lets hope it doesn't happen to Sheila the Scot." Others laugh, but Mrs Scott doesn't.

After lunch we visit Saint Sophia, built by the Emperor Justinian in the sixth century and for long the greatest church in Christendom. Cathedral, mosque and now a museum, it rises above the city, its pink-painted façade glowing in the bright sunshine. The inside with its magnificent dome is so beautiful that for a few minutes we are stunned into silence. Not so the crowds round us. Our guide, Sule, has a very quiet voice and nowhere in this enormous building can we hear a word she is saying.

We wander round on our own, and then walk up, not steps, but a winding passage to the gallery. The mosaics still glitter, and the faces on the Deisis, Christ, John the Baptist and the Virgin Mary seem almost living as they look sadly down at us.

Then we cross the road to Justinian's other great masterpiece – the basilica cistern. A huge underground reservoir – its roof supported by over three hundred pillars arranged in rows. The scale is breath-taking. Beethoven's Fifth blares out from loudspeakers as we walk round on wooden platforms just above the water. Even the crowds don't spoil the atmosphere. The lights are dim, the ceiling is dripping and ghostly carp glide through the water. A head of Medusa is carved on one of the columns: upside down. It's all very spooky. "Just the place for a murder," says Mr Grey. Well, they did film some of *From Russia With Love* here.

We are all utterly exhausted and totter back to the hotel – pestered nonstop on the way by little boys selling strips of postcards and guide books.

Monday: Istanbul – Antalya

Gloria is grumpy at breakfast. "This is supposed to be a holiday," she says. "I don't need all this education." Sheila Scott says they never have to get up this early with other travel companies. Fishing Socks shows them his mosquito repellant: "In case we go near any more mosques." They aren't amused.

But this morning it's the boat trip up the Bosphorus that they've been looking forward to and complaining that it's only for half a day. "I hope you've got sea-sick pills for us," says Sheila.

As we embark on a small boat it is pouring with rain. We head across the strait to a waterside café on the Asian side to sample apple tea, and while we are sitting there a huge Russian tanker passes on it's way to the Black Sea and its wash sweeps through the café. Everyone leaps onto tables, none faster than Mr Grey with his wooden leg, and stay there until the waves subside. We then continue our cruise with the windows steamed up inside, and rain pouring down outside. Everyone had wanted a full day's cruise, but now they don't.

We finally disembark and set off for the Grand Bazaar with its maze of passages and stalls. Sule tells us to avoid the main streets and concentrate on side alleys for better bargains.

We are given half an hour to wander and buy, and it's a miracle that we all manage to meet at a small saleroom for a carpet show. We sit round sipping apple tea watching a slick display of carpets – most of them modern. Several people buy, but Lord Palmer (tall, elegant and aged, like his wife) says that they are all too small for their house.

Back at the hotel we collect our bags and set off to the airport for our flight to Antalya. Mr Whitworth has lost his ticket, but is quite unconcerned, and it turns up in his wallet. We arrive at Antalya in a thunderstorm. The luggage is dumped by porters outside the terminal and elderly Lord Palmer, helped by the driver, loads it onto our bus in the pouring rain. Everyone else sits inside the bus looking on.

Tuesday: Antalya – Termessos

Our hotel is in the old part of the city overlooking the small Roman harbour, now overshadowed by high-rise buildings that seem to stretch as far as the distant mountains.

We are off to Termessos – a site that involves a steep climb. So Wooden Leg and Fishing socks decide not to come. Mr Innes is last to board the bus because he is trying to explain to the hall porter that the Union Jack outside the hotel is flying upside down. The porter, not surprisingly, doesn't understand.

The city of Termessos lies unexcavated and overgrown above a high mountain pass, reached by a twenty minute walk up a stony path. Its income came from raising taxes and from olive oil, for which there was an "olio-duct" instead of an aqueduct – a channel that ran right down to the coast. It was inhabited by a nation noted for its ferocity. So much so that Alexander the Great gave it a wide berth as he swept through the area.

It was abandoned about 600 AD and rediscovered by a British naturalist in 1842. The buildings have been smashed up by earthquakes, which means a lot of scrambling over rocks and loose scree to reach the theatre set against a breathtaking backdrop of high, forested mountains. We sit admiring the view and don't notice enormous black clouds coming up behind us. Flashes of lightning, thunder and then rain. It's terrifically dramatic. There is nowhere to shelter and the rocks have become slippery, so we slither down the mountainside, arriving at our bus soaked through and covered in mud.

"Not a great success," says Sheila.

Off to lunch at a fish farm. Sule is enthusiastic, but some of the party aren't. "I never eat trout that hasn't been caught with a fly," says Fishing Socks. Others agree and settle for Spaghetti Bolognese.

We have a free afternoon in Antalya where we quickly explore the old city and spend a long time having drinks in a little café overlooking the old harbour.

Wednesday: Antalya – Phaselis

Another boat trip, this time on the sea, to the ruined port of Phaselis – in ancient times a pirates' lair, easily defensible, under the slopes of Mount Olympus. Its ruins are from Roman and Byzantine times, not particularly interesting, but are set romantically among pine trees and little beaches.

Fishing Socks has entered into the spirit of the cruise by appearing in what he calls his Pirates of Penzance outfit. Blue and white striped tee shirt, red spotted handkerchief round neck, shorts and long stockings, all topped with a panama hat. The wind is cold and the rest of us sit in the stern huddled under blankets.

Lunch is cooked on board. It's small bits of fish in batter. "Farmed trout again," they say, and leave it.

We reach a small bay where the more energetic are going to disembark and walk over the hills. A rubber dinghy takes them to the shore, but unfortunately it has no engine and no oars, so the captain's young son dives into the water and pushes it along. It's difficult to time the leap from the boat to the beach without getting wet and everybody is soaked.

The walkers have walked along paths through woods and meadows and meet us at a little jetty where we can disembark safely. Then we explore independently, bumping into each other round every corner. Having "done" the site we have a "sunset walk along the beach for an early dinner at the Sundance restaurant."

It is a half-hour walk and Sule, (Gloria will call her Shula, like the character in *The Archers*) says we will have to paddle through the sea which is lapping the bottom of a cliff.

She takes off her shoes, tucks up her skirt and wades through water up to her thighs. Nobody follows. The alternative is a steep climb up and over the headland, but it's a military area and we have to crawl through a gap under the barbed wire fence.

The way up is precipitous and the way down adventurous and rocky. It's very tricky for Wooden Leg who says nothing, but easy for Gunn and Scott, who don't stop complaining.

We pick our way through driftwood along the shore and arrive at a deep estuary with no way of crossing it. Just as people were wishing they hadn't come, a tractor and trailer drive through the water towards us. All aboard. There's a bad moment when we come to get off because Mr Innes jumps down and his corduroy jacket gets caught on a nail and he is left dangling until it slowly rips apart.

The Sundance is a wooden chalet with a welcome fire and we sit round two large tables drinking raki and eating kebabs grilled on a barbecue. Everyone is asleep on the journey back to Antalya.

Thursday: Antalya – Arycanda – Myra – Antalya

It's a very early start for a bus ride westwards. Most are still sleepy, but Sheila Scott, complaining loudly, soon wakes them up. We are heading for Arycanda, a spectacular site, romantic and atmospheric, right off the beaten track with no other tourists.

The city is built on five long terraces on the side of a mountain, and in early May its grey stone walls are set off by bright green grass, untrampled by hordes of visitors. It is one of the most ancient Lycian cities, staying fat and prosperous all through Roman and Christian times, finally abandoned in the eleventh century, when the remaining inhabitants moved down hill.

We walk up through the site: baths, gymnasium, villas, odeon and ruins of the main surviving church with traces of mosaic floors. The theatre is on the highest terrace, just below the stadium – a perfect place to sit and rest. This captive audience is too tempting for Mr Innes who takes centre stage and starts declaiming lines from Medea – in Greek of course. He tells us that when he recited this in the theatre in Taormina, Harold Macmillan, who was in the party, stepped onto the stage and carried on where he left off. This inspires others. Wooden Leg struggles through Masefield's *Cargoes,* and Gloria, not to be outdone, starts on *Jabberwocky*, but dries up after three lines and Mr Innes takes over. Sheila says she would have liked to recite *The Owl and the Pussycat* but couldn't remember it.

Lunch is at the custodian's house, cooked by his wife, and we sit on their verandah looking down the valley at the view below. Miles and miles of plastic greenhouses glinting in the bright sun.

We drive back to Antalya along the coast road via Myra, and admire the rock tombs cut in the cliffs giving a sort of honeycomb background to the town. At the entrance to the square we are greeted by a huge, plastic model of Father Christmas, looking particularly out of place, but reminding us that this is the birthplace of St Nicholas. Behind him is the church with its fourth century foundations.

In 1087 the body of the saint was stolen by seamen from Bari in Italy and the bones went to the newly built cathedral, there to be venerated as the patron saint of sailors. In the nineteenth century Czar Nicholas I of Russia restored the church and it became a place of pilgrimage for Russians. More recently early frescoes have been restored and the whole building has been smartened up.

We spend a short time here and a long time in the market outside buying jewellery, pashminas and tee shirts. The men, soon bored, sit on a wall surrounded by a pack of wild dogs, while the women drink apple tea and bargain with stall-holders. Many buy necklaces and rings. "Aren't you buying anything?" somebody asks Lady Palmer. She spreads out her elegant ring-choked fingers. "I've no room for any more." Sheila is given "very special price for very old lady." Not pleased.

Friday: Antalya

Mr Scott, who has had several replacement hips, puts his foot up on a chair, ties his shoelace, and his hip comes out of its socket. He is in agony, not helped by his wife telling him off for being so stupid.

I call an ambulance, and suddenly we leave the tourist world for real life in a hospital where nobody speaks English except the doctors. Everyone is chewing gum and everyone looks like a porter until it comes to lifting Mr Scott onto the x-ray bed. Sheila and I have to heave his fifteen stone. (Thank goodness he has recently lost three stone). He is wheeled off to the operating theatre and we wait outside the door in a dark passage. There is nowhere to sit, but after a search we find a long plank of wood which we balance on an upturned bucket and sit at either end like a see-saw. "Don't get up without warning me," I say to Sheila, "Or I will go for six."

A sobbing woman sitting on the floor tells Sheila not to talk so loudly, and she responds by giving the woman an enormous hug, saying people aren't touched enough nowadays.

We wait for a long time. Suddenly Mr Scott is wheeled out of the operating theatre. Sheila leaps up and I go for six.

The hip is back in place and he is pushed into a ward towards an empty bed – only just empty, as the last occupant must have recently died. The bedclothes are rumpled and on the bedside table is a pair of false teeth, spectacles and some screwed up tissues.

We ask for pillows and clean sheets, but none are forthcoming, so Sheila goes and rummages through cupboards, bringing out dirty rolls of old sheets, but no pillows.

Mr Scott would like a drink of water, but there isn't any because your family is expected to bring you food and drink. Luckily I have an orange in my pocket which he eats gratefully. There are eight beds squashed into the small ward, and each bed has about ten relations standing round, either crying or shouting.

There is no sign of any nurses and he needs a loo bottle. The phrase book is no help, but Sheila – no inhibitions – nobbles a doctor and demonstrates. I, feeling somewhat embarrassed, offer to go and buy some food, but the hospital isn't near any shops.

The surgeon wants to keep Jim here for three weeks, but Sheila insists on discharge tomorrow, when we are flying home.

We get back to the hotel to find everyone has had a good day at two ancient sites: Perge and Aspendos – impressive ruins among wild flowers. Mr Innes recited *Ozymandias* in the amphitheatre at Aspendos. Fishing Socks says "We saw Ionic columns and Corinthian columns, but no Doric. Alas poor Doric." He laughs so much that he repeats it over and over again. It was funny the first time.

Saturday: Antalya – Istanbul – Heathrow

Sheila and I make an early visit to the hospital to collect Jim, who has made a remarkable recovery and is best friends with everyone in the ward. "Jim gets on with everyone," says Sheila.

Our flight to Heathrow is via Istanbul, which means we have time to kill in Istanbul so we drive to the Blue Mosque which we missed before. Some are keen to miss it now, so sit outside in the sun while the rest of us join a long queue at the side door.

Sultan Ahmet I – in the early seventeenth century – wanted to build a mosque that would surpass Justinian's achievement, but a thousand years later he still couldn't beat the dome of Saint Sophia.

This mosque is much less ambitious, and the massive pillars holding it up are less elegant than Justinian's, but it is a magnificent, light, spacious building with the blue Iznik tiles round the walls giving it its name.

We have a boozy last lunch on way to the airport and afterwards Sule and I go and find the coach. The driver and several other men, covered in oil, are lying under it. They won't admit anything is wrong, but it's pretty obvious it won't be moving in a hurry.

I have to act quickly so I persuade another coach driver, whose passengers are still having lunch, to take us the couple of miles to the airport. We move the luggage but time is getting on and the boozy mood soon evaporates. I telephone the airport to say we are on way, but when we get there we find the plane is overbooked and our seats have been re-allocated.

Bad moment. I contact an airline official who double-checks and says they can take fourteen passengers if they hurry. There is a stampede. "Our dogs are expecting us," they shout as they push each other aside in their haste to get through the barrier. Mrs Gunn hits Lord Palmer with her trolley and draws blood. Wooden Leg is felled. Mr Innes quietly nips through the barrier unnoticed.

The nicest people are left behind. Fishing Socks – always good-natured – looks up at the departure board and suggests various destinations: Delhi, Addis Ababa, Qatar. Where shall we go? We somehow find an empty flight to Vienna with a connection to London. Club Class and champagne all the way.

I take my report to our Travel Company, expecting to get the sack. They couldn't have been less interested. A Guest Lecturer and Tour Manager in Eastern Turkey had broken the golden rule: they had fallen out with each other.

Romania
Lost Shepherdess

~ June ~

Cast List

Lady Burton	*Not a hair out of place*
Patricia Evans	*Shepherdess from Wales*
Rev. Reg	*Retired school chaplain*
Catherine Weston	*Chaotic Kate*
Doctor and Wife	*From Lincolnshire*
And others	

Friday: Gatwick – Bucharest – Cimpulung Moldovenesc

The Romanians are the proud descendents of Roman legionaries who were cut off when the barbarian hordes poured over the frontier. They are a Latin people, surrounded by a sea of Slavs. So instead of the great Slav soul they have the Latin Temperament, which excuses them from dull things like being on time – but does make them a lot jollier.

Our early tours were something of an experiment. It was only a few years after the revolution and we didn't know what to expect. The pattern we evolved was to combine walks in the northern Carpathian Mountains with visits to the painted churches of Bucovina – which were becoming famous having just been made World Heritage Sites. The clients had been told this, and some were seasoned travellers ready to try something new, others were not.

Some, such as the Shepherdess from Wales, were perhaps a bit too resolute. She is first to arrive at the check-in desk. She has left her sheep behind and hopes they will be all right. Bo-Peep? No. Tall and skinny, wearing a cowboy hat and cords rather than a poke bonnet and crinoline, and obviously not a worrier. Good.

The doctor and his wife are next. Most doctors turn out to be engineers, but this one is medical, which might be useful although he looks pretty ancient. He sits bent forward with his head resting on a thumb-stick while his wife reads out clues from the crossword, both looking comfortable in each other's company.

When we land at Bucharest the queues at immigration are long and there's no sign of Tad, our agent, who has promised to whisk us through formalities. The clients come through controls slowly and dig out their luggage from a heap piled haphazardly on the floor. Rev. Reg is the last as the computer has broken down. He has a shock of white hair contrasting oddly with a ruddy complexion and watery blue eyes. That, together with a rough, tweed suit and viyella checked shirt complete with tie, gives no clue to his profession, or rather vocation.

We wait for ages, watching his frustration, but eventually find Tad and Carolina (guide) on the other side of customs and set off in a bus for a tour of Bucharest. It was once "the Paris of the East," but that was before the communist president Ceaucescu got his hands on it and destroyed a quarter of the old city. We drive through street after street where old houses have been torn down and new concrete horrors erected. Just occasionally we get a glimpse of a few houses that have been spared – sprawling nineteenth-century villas in leafy gardens.

We go to an open-air village museum and walk round in the heat. It's rather pointless looking at these model houses since soon we will be seeing the real things; but we have to fill in time before our train journey north to the painted churches.

Our guide, Carolina, has short dark hair showing off high cheek bones – quite good-looking and smartly dressed – I suspect from a family that flourished in pre-communist days. She is well-informed to a fault especially about economics – a characteristic of guides in ex-communist countries – but redeemed by an ample sense of humour. Tad, the agent, is an engineer by profession, but more committed to showing tourists the beauties of his country. They take us to a restaurant in a cellar for a huge peasanty dinner that nobody can finish, and then to the station. We pile into sleepers, singletons doubling up. They aren't too cramped, and there are clean sheets and basins with cold water. So far so good.

Saturday: Cimpulung Moldovensc – Moldovita – Sucevita

We get to Cimpulung station at 5.15am. The train bumped and rattled intolerably, so no one has slept. Everyone looks bleary except Lady Burton who has to protect her delicate skin under make-up and large hats. Her husband was an ambassador, and she keeps up the manners and style that went with her role as consort.

We arrive at our hotel – a hideous tower block near the station and one of our less seasoned travellers, Chaotic Kate, announces she has left her passport on the train. I'm not surprised – she is travelling with three suitcases and several plastic bags stuffed with papers. She has a pudgy face – eyes sinking into the pudge, and untidy fair hair falling out of hairpins. She needn't have told us that her shabby clothes come from charity shops.

An unwelcoming cashier has arrived early to change money. Then we find our dreary rooms with peeling paint and dirty carpets. But the water is boiling hot and after a bath and change and vast breakfast of bread and jam we are ready to go.

The doctor asks to have quiet word with me. His wife, who has had a double mastectomy, has left her prosthesis on the train. Could I please get it back? Prosthesis? Of course, her false boobs.

We are joined by our walking guide, Nicolae, tough and bearded. He teaches carpentry at a local school and leads walks in his spare time.

We go by coach to the monastery of Moldavita, painted white and surrounded by a high wall. The church stands on its own inside a compound and is covered in paintings – as bright and fresh as the artists left them nearly five hundred years ago.

The monasteries of Bucovina date from the heroic age of the real Prince Dracula (Vlad Dracul) who kept the Turks at bay. Every church has a painting of the Fall of Constantinople, as a warning of what might happen if the people dropped their guard. The paintings are not just bright and clearly visible – they are beautiful, based on Byzantine models. Nobody knows how they have survived the centuries of wind and weather: the eaves and high surrounding walls must have given some protection, but the experts are still baffled.

We drive to a nearby village "to embark on open-air mountain train, for spectacular views to Secriev, 14 kms away" – a small black engine belching black smoke pulling trucks for logs, with a small enclosed cattle truck for us at the back. All aboard. Every few minutes we stop and men get out of the engine to hit the wheels with hammers. Are we too heavy? We crawl up the hill puffing through thick woods with a forestry track beside it. So where's this spectacular scenery? We start and stop, start and stop again – this time for fifteen minutes to fill up the engine with water from a stream. When we reach the top the train will no doubt turn round and come back the same way. But will we ever get to the top?

Eventually we all decide to get out and start walking back along the track that follows the railway. Suddenly the sky turns black and there is a terrific thunderstorm: before we get to the shelter of the trees we are soaked through. At last the train is heard, and rumbles into sight. It has left the log carriages at the top, turned round, and now black smoke is pouring into our carriage. There are smuts everywhere, which the doctor says will shorten our lives by twenty years.

At 2pm we get off the train – three hours from the beginning. Carolina says we will find a nice spot for a picnic (in the pouring rain), while the doctor asks if we can stop at a bar. We find a not-quite-ideal picnic place under the awning of a café by the side of a road with heavy lorries rumbling past, but at least there is masses to eat and drink. Afterwards we set off in the bus for a twenty minute drive to the start of our walk which will now be cut to two hours because of time spent in the train. We get out and start plodding along the road in the rain. Suddenly our guide plunges downhill into the bushes and we follow, with Rev. Reg (white trainers) complaining loudly. A gypsy appears and tries to help the doctor (white trousers and white trainers) down the slippery slope. Both go for six – black trousers, black trainers.

We end up at the monastery of Sucevita soaking wet and covered in mud. On the outside of the church there is a stunning scene of Jacob's Ladder, but we're all too cold to appreciate it. Inside, Carolina tells us about Romanian monasteries. The vows aren't necessarily for life: it is quite all right to be a nun for ten years, leave to marry and have children, and then come back in old age. One of their roles is to help with unemployment: a lad who can't get a job can sign on as a lay-brother and work at the monastery for a few years, until the job-market looks up. In these villages through forty years of communism, the Orthodox Church maintained its central place.

Back at the hotel by a quarter-to-eight. Rev. Reg is in a rage and won't come down to dinner. Chaotic Kate goes to the station with Carolina to collect her passport, which has been found, but there is no sign of the missing boob. Carolina says they wouldn't have known what it was. We all go to bed exhausted, wondering why we came.

Sunday: Cimpulung Moldovenesc – Rarau Peak

It looks better today. The sun is lurking behind clouds, and so is the Rev. Reg who will meet us later with Carolina, while we set off with Nicolae. There is a short drive to the beginning of the walk, and then we start uphill through a village, past men walking down to church in traditional dress and hats. There are animals wandering freely – hens, pigs, geese, cows and horses. And we admire the wooden houses built in different styles and colour, all vaguely like Swiss chalets. Branches of lime trees are arched over the gate posts, to celebrate Pentecost. The doctor sees a steep hill ahead and turns back to join Carolina.

It is a really beautiful walk across grassy meadows with long views in all directions, but it doesn't last. Soon it is uphill through pine woods and it begins to rain. It pours. The doctor's wife lives in East Anglia, and isn't used to steep hills, and hasn't even got proper walking boots. She stops every few steps to get her breath and I walk beside her while the rest of the party press ahead. She'll never make it to the top so I flag down a car coming up the track behind us and push her in.

We arrive at the cabana at Rarau Peak (spectacular views on fine day) for lunch, soaked to the skin in spite of waterproof-guaranteed anoraks. Only Lady Burton remains dry, her manners and mascara intact.

Lunch lasts for three hours – most of it waiting to be served. My hands are so cold that I keep my gloves on throughout. We have soup, polenta with two different cheeses, and unbelievably tough mutton. The Shepherdess from Wales doesn't recognise the bones and wonders if it really is sheep. We drink hot spiced wine, but nobody wants to wait for coffee.

We walk downhill to meet Carolina and the non-walkers, who have been waiting an hour and a half and are not pleased. We walk uphill in the rain to look at a simple church which is locked. A monk appears and takes the key from under the doormat – which reminds Chaotic Kate that she has forgotten to tell Brown Owl where she has hidden her own church key, and must telephone England tonight.

We get back to the hotel at a quarter to eight. A quick change and out to a new private restaurant where our life is saved by a new discovery – tuica or tweaker, the local plum brandy. We have a delicious dinner, entertained by musicians and dancers in traditional dress. Afterwards we all join in. If someone spreads a handkerchief at your feet you have to kneel down and kiss them. Great fun.

Monday: Cimpulung Moldovensc – Humor – Voronet – Durau

Our hotel is in the middle of the town surrounded by other modern buildings, all made of concrete, grey and featureless and stained with green slime from leaking water pipes – a sad contrast with the wooden houses in the country. Beside our hotel there is an open-air market, and for a few pence we buy bags of cherries and strawberries.

We check out of the hotel, and drive through villages and rolling country to another monastery called Humor. Each house we pass has a well with a shingle roof and the gardens are full of lilac and early geraniums.

It is Whit-Monday and at the church we have come to look at there is a service, so we go on to Voronet – the gem among painted churches, which Carolina says looks at its best at sunset. The Abbess of the convent appears and asks us to sing a hymn. Rev. Reg whips his congregation into action and we all sing "Holy, Holy, Holy" – Hymn 162 I remember, in my school English Hymnal.

We have a picnic in a garden by a river. An old lady bent double, digging up horseradish, shouts at us, and we think we are trespassing, but Carolina says "She's only asking if you want to help her."

After lunch we set off for three-hour walk to Slatina – another monastery. Some stay behind with Carolina to meet us on the bus at the end of the walk. Nicolae leads while I walk at the back as usual; it's uphill through pines, and at the top there are fantastic views across blue mountains, then down muddy tracks crisscrossed with the fresh diggings of wild boars and prints of bears, large and small. Nicolae says that bears are particularly dangerous when with cubs.

As usual we arrive late at the convent at Slatina where the others have been waiting. But where is the Shepherdess? Carolina looks aghast and says she was photographing sheep for ten minutes after lunch and would catch us up. Carolina disapproved and told her that they would wait for half an hour and if she didn't reach us quickly, must turn round and come back.

Now we have no idea where she is. Did she go back to Voronet? Did she get a lift to the Convent at Durau, where we are spending the next two nights? Is she lost in the woods, or had a confrontation with a boar or a bear?

By now it is after 7pm and the drive to Durau is over two hours. Carolina is worrying whether the nuns will keep dinner for us.

We decide that Nicolae and I will get a taxi back to Voronet to look for the Shepherdess while the others go on to Durau. Although it isn't a long walk over the hill, it's thirty miles round by road. The driver goes like the clappers, scattering cows, horses, chickens and pigs who as always are wandering over the road. No sign of her in the town or monastery, so we go back to the picnic place and start walking back up the hill. Still no sign.

"Could she have got to the convent at Slatina on her own?" I suggest.

"No way," says Nicolae.

Telephoning convents is not easy, and anyway telephones are switched off at 9pm, so we drive on to Durau arriving at midnight to hear she is safe with the nuns at Slatina, where we ended the walk. She arrived half an hour after we left. Phew! When she set off to catch us up she could hear our voices, only a hundred yards ahead, but three hundred feet above her. She soon got lost but sensibly followed a stream downhill till she came to a village. She had left her itinerary in the bus and had no idea what convent we were walking to, or where we were staying. She flagged down a car and said "Monastair." By a curious coincidence it was the same car that had rescued the doctor's wife the day before – they must be getting used to the daft English. They drove her to Slatina, which luckily was the only monastery in the area.

Tuesday: Durau

Our convent at Durau is over-run with builders. The rooms are basic and smell of damp concrete: but although the mattresses are lumpy, there are no bedside lights and the hot water is fitful, everyone likes it. There are wonderful views towards the mountains and the nuns are very welcoming. Hot chocolate for breakfast, because nuns don't drink tea or coffee – too stimulating.

It's a beautiful day and we set off walking down the road outside the convent. We keep walking and are overtaken by cars and lorries. There is magnificent scenery all around. "Why aren't we walking through that?" they ask. We pass men in hats scything in fields and women in headscarves hoeing gardens. There are more workers raking hay with huge wooden rakes and hanging it on posts to dry: they look rather like standing stones dotted about the fields.

We arrive at Lake Bicaz and find the best available picnic place is a grassy mound with no shade. The lake gently laps against the shore washing up old shoes, rusty tins, plastic cups and syringes. Nicolae says it's his birthday and produces two bottles of tweaker from a leather hold-all. The Rev. Reg has saved a huge bottle of wine from dinner last night.

I reckon that the lakeside walk in afternoon will be rather dull, so suggest that keen walkers go back to the hotel and walk with Nicolae in the mountains. I lead the others round the lake – even duller than I imagined.

Back at the convent, Carolina has driven three hours each way and brought back our Shepherdess. She had enjoyed a lovely time at Slatina with the nuns, who didn't want to let her go. They called her La Perdita – the lost one.

The mountaineers return by 7.30pm having had a splendid walk. We have a delicious dinner of rabbit pie and home-grown vegetables, washed down with tweaker (specially ordered for us), and wine grown by the nuns on the estate.

Wednesday/Thursday   Durau – Agapia – overnight train – Bucharest

The nuns have bought coffee and tea especially for us, and after a hearty breakfast we set off in the bus, with packed lunches, for the monastery of Secu. We avoid oxen and horses pulling carts loaded with long logs sticking out at the back. Carolina says they've all been banned from using the roads as they cause accidents. Some of us stay in the bus as usual, while the walkers carry their picnics uphill through woods. A beggar at a gate looks very happy counting his takings after we have passed by. The sky looks threatening and soon the heavens open. Where on earth will we have the picnic?

We get to Sihla monastery at the top of a hill. It's under restoration, covered in wooden scaffolding with mud everywhere, churned up by bulldozers. The workers are sitting eating lunch at a long table under the eaves of the monastery. We are welcomed by the monks who invite us to sit at another table (with a tablecloth), and we start on our picnic. The monks bring out enamel bowls and mugs and then huge tureens of soup, plates of scrambled eggs and jugs of camomile tea. They won't take any payment, but donations to the church are gratefully accepted.

We carry on for what is meant to be a three hour walk to Agapia, but takes only half that time. On the way, out of a pretty green house, leaps a professor of French who waylays us for twenty minutes. We look at the monastery at Agapia (under restoration) and meet the bus with the non-walkers. There is time for coffee in a café, where the French professor re-appears and becomes a slight bore.

Off to a pilgrimage house for dinner, but far too much time to kill before the train to Bucharest, so two fours of bridge are formed, and the rest play Old Maid or go and look for wine for dinner. This is a hard-drinking area – tweaker on tap, but not much else.

Dinner in a basement with dim lighting that flickers and goes out altogether when people walk heavily overhead. Delicious parsley soup with dumplings, smoked sausages with beans, and pancakes doused with tweaker. "Crêpes Tweakettes," says some wag.

We set off to Suceava to catch the 11.15pm sleeper train to Bucharest, and arrive in a storm. We stand on an open platform and get soaked. Everyone is dreading another night in uncomfortable bunks – Chaotic Kate has already nearly flipped. The train arrives, but where are our sleepers? There is one sleeping compartment, but no sign of our whole carriage. We push our way into the train, looking out for the doctor who may need help up the steps. Needn't have worried. The least agile of the party, he dives quickly into the one empty sleeper before anyone notices.

Carolina has a slanging match with an official, who thinks that the other sleepers must be the other end of the train, but we can't walk through the train yet, because there are secret letters in the post van which will be removed at the next station. Rupert of Henzau, says someone. We stand in the corridor with our luggage piled up on the muddy wet floor. Carolina bursts into tears.

After the next station she meets an official. The sleeper is definitely at the other end of the train. "You will all be in your beds in fifteen minutes." The thought of an uncomfortable sleeper is now very attractive and we start walking down the corridor. Very narrow. Very long. Squeeze past people standing, stepping on their toes and knocking them with our bags. Stop. Start. After forty minutes we reach the far end of the train. No sleeper.

People settle into carriages and Rev. Reg sits alone in an empty one which is awash with water.

Carolina says the sleeper is definitely being put on at the next station but one. "Get ready to move." No sign of it. "Next stop," she says. We are all resigned to spending the night sitting up.

By now the train has filled up and there are very few spare seats. The ticket collector says there are more seats up the other end. Carolina and I start walking. People are standing all along corridor. Carolina says she never travels on trains because of the class of person you find on them. Picnics in some compartments, gambling in others, singing, drinking and smoking everywhere. Occasional glimpses of our party looking totally out of place among their rough and ready travelling companions. Two couples have managed to keep an entire first class compartment to themselves and are stretched out comfortably across it, while several single women have claimed another and have a shouting match with an enormously fat woman who has come to claim her reserved seat. She goes to fetch the guard who takes one look at the opposition and finds her a different seat. Rev. Reg has been turned out of his water-logged compartment, which soon fills up with passengers. Chaotic Kate is also turned out, and they join our procession towards the emptier end of the train. Carolina, sobbing, puts her bag down every few seconds and says she is going to complain to the head of the railways for ruining her nerves, but we keep going until we reach the end of the train. No empty seats.

Carolina produces bottle of Romanian champagne and we four settle down on suitcases outside a lavatory. Chaotic Kate pulls a bottle of wine out of a plastic bag. Rev. Reg pulls *The Odyssey* out of his. A large gypsy comes to our loo to have a wash, but the basin flies off the wall and the tap gushes cold water all over the floor and down the corridor. We move hastily and find another insalubrious pitch.

The train is due in to Bucharest at 6.30am, but it arrives at 5.30. It's very difficult to get everyone off the train. We are all looking incredibly bleary except Lady Burton – clean as a whistle and fresh as a daisy.

Tad is there to meet us. He knew about our earlier arrival and has informed the bus and the hotel. No bus, so we bundle into taxis which race each other at high speed to the Lebada hotel. It is large and cool and very expensive, in a beautiful setting over-looking a lake.

Our bedraggled party stands in the hall while Carolina is obviously having problems with Reception. She turns round and announces breakfast in forty-five minutes, and rooms in three hours: the bedraggled party is too shattered even to moan.

Things suddenly look up. Breakfast is announced straight away and there will be some rooms available in a minute. Those who have had the worst night should get their rooms first. It doesn't work out like that: the least deserving – those who slept best and are on the ball – push to the front. Everyone else waits patiently and cheerfully. By 8.30 everyone has a room and at 2pm we meet for lunch, clean and rested, everyone having his own train story to tell.

We walk through the Old Quarter to the Manuc Inn – a genuine nineteenth-century caravanserai round a huge courtyard in which gypsies are singing and dancing. Some of our party wish they were staying here, since it looks so romantic and real. Carolina is horrified. How could people prefer something so primitive to our grand, modern hotel?

Tad appears at dinner with a bottle of champagne for everyone and a little note thanking us all – nearly all – for keeping our sense of humour.

Friday: Bucharest – London

We check out of the hotel and visit Ceausescu's palace. This gigantic monsterpiece – the House of the People – is supposed to be the third biggest building in the world. Everything is on a huge scale – cold and soulless but impressive. Enormous concert halls and conference rooms. Vast passages. A few fine touches – carving by craftsman on the wooden doors and huge carpets woven by nuns from the scaffold-clad monastery we visited yesterday.

All the surrounding streets lead up to it, lined with hideous concrete buildings. There are fountains along the central reservations – not of course working, and falling to bits.

We go on to the Cotroceni Palace – a former royal residence which seems small and cosy by comparison. The short-lasting monarchy included a couple of solid German kings, one playboy, and two remarkable queens – Elizabeth, who under the name of Carmen Sylva was a poet and romantic writer, and Marie, the grand-daughter of Queen Victoria, whose charm drummed up sympathy for her country during the first world war – reflected in Romania's gains at the peace treaty.

And so to the airport. Chaotic Kate says "I've enjoyed every minute. That's what holidays ought to be like."

Cyprus
Shipwreck

~ October ~

Cast List

Colonel and Mrs Horsman	*Ancient, doddery couple*
Dr Briggs	*Retired female psychiatrist*
Mr and Mrs Faber-Jones	*Accountant from Surrey*
Mr and Mrs Innes	*Retired classics master. Came without wife to Turkey in May*
Tweedledum and Tweedledee	*From the north*
And others	

Cyprus is the island of love, the home of the goddess Venus. Mark Anthony gave it to Cleopatra as a wedding present, a local Byzantine tyrant kidnapped Richard the Lionheart's fiancée (a bad career move), and the Crusaders set up a romantic kingdom. The Venetians diddled them out of it.

In 1570 the Turkish Sultan, Selim the Sot, conquered the island (in a sober moment) and it remained an Ottoman backwater till it passed peacefully to the British three hundred years later. After which, with the Empire crumbling, there was a violent campaign to get the British out. Unfortunately independence was followed by a civil war between the Greek majority and the Turkish minority.

In 1974 the Turkish army invaded Cyprus. They had some excuse – the civil war continued and something had to be done. The Turks did it their way: they grabbed the best third of the island, there was a short, brutal exchange of population (or ethnic cleansing) and the two sides settled down to glare at each other harmlessly, with a United Nations force between them. Since then, the Greek side, recognised by the world as the legitimate government, grew rich and prosperous: the Turkish side, recognised by no one much, stayed poor and charming under a (benign) military occupation. The border was partly opened in 2007 – several years after this tour – and although the two sides can't agree, at least exiles from each sector can now visit their old homes.

Saturday: Heathrow – Kyrenia

Colonel Horsman is agitated. He looks every inch the colonel: grey hair with dead-straight parting, moustache, tweed suit with regimental tie. "I'm afraid my wife is a bad arriver," he says. Mrs Horsman is sitting hunched up on a suitcase glaring. She has a beaky nose and sunken eyes in her over-powdered face. Her skin looks thin and bloodless; her lips are almost white. Not surprising as she must be well over eighty. The plane is already delayed by an hour, and as she has been up since dawn she can be excused her bad mood.

The flight is tedious. North Cyprus is not recognised by any country other than Turkey, so to get round flight restrictions we land at Izmir – or Smyrna – as Mr Innes calls it. We wait for an hour while the plane is refuelled, the flight number is changed and we become a legitimate domestic flight.

Long delays at immigration when we do land in Cyprus because a flight from Istanbul has arrived a few minutes before us.

We arrive at our hotel in Kyrenia well past midnight and are offered soup and fish and chips while the bags are sorted out. Surely people don't want fish and chips at this hour of night? They do.

Sunday: Kyrenia

I am always surprised that on the first morning, however late we have arrived at our destination, most people are down for breakfast and eager to get going. A couple of exceptions – Dr Briggs has overslept as she thought the clocks went back two hours instead of forward and Mrs Horsman's false teeth have fallen onto the marble floor and shattered.

Our guide Osman appears: a small man with a red face and a thick moustache – dressed in crisp white shirt and jeans. He speaks perfect English which is not surprising, having worked in a sandwich bar in Finsbury Park, but he is well-read, knowledgeable and has great charm. He is also a terrific name-dropper, asking me in a loud voice if I have recently seen various aristocrats who have been on past tours.

The group assembles in the usual array of summer-holiday-abroad clothes (smelling rather musty), unbecoming hats and a variety of shoes – some sensible, some not. Two large, round couples have bonded quickly. Is it because the husbands look almost identical in too-tight shorts, loose shirts over flopping stomachs, white ankle socks and sandals? Tweedledum and Tweedledee.

The Horsmans go to the dentist, but return immediately as they forgot to take the teeth with them. The rest of us set off round the town. Dr Briggs, small and stout with straight, black hair and a fringe nearly covering her eyes, can only walk with two sticks, very slowly, but has no inhibitions about holding up the party.

We wander round the pretty harbour shaped like a horseshoe, with lines of fishing boats and yachts moored at its edge. The original warehouses surrounding the harbour have long been converted into shops or restaurants and the area is closed to traffic, so our party straggle happily all over the place in the bright sunshine. Mr Faber-Jones, who did his National Service in Cyprus, trips happily down memory lane recalling week-ends at the Harbour Club presided over by famous hosts – Roy and Judy Finlay.

Kyrenia castle, standing above the harbour, was built over many centuries by Byzantines, Crusaders and finally Venetians. The main attraction is the shipwreck museum where a 2,300 year-old Greek trading vessel is on display, together with its cargo of almonds, still in their shells.

We explore the castle, including the dungeons which display waxwork models of Christian guards inflicting unspeakable tortures on their Turkish prisoners. Up and down steps, in and out of chambers and onto the ramparts with Dr Briggs in front feeling her way with her sticks, the rest of the party unable to pass.

After a stodgy lunch (moussaka, rice and chips) in a restaurant beside the harbour, we walk through the town, hoping to see the Folk Museum which is closed and the Icon Museum – also closed. However, St Andrew's, the Anglican church is open. (The Greek churches were all shut down when the Turks invaded). It is a simple whitewashed building recently expanded to accommodate the growing community of expatriates. A Pakistani student stands at the lectern reading the bible out loud, and says he is looking for a Christian family to stay with. "Why not try the vicar?" I say. "Good idea, I knew I would find the answer in church."

Back at the hotel, Mrs Horsman, now re-teethed, is bitterly regretting this holiday. Was going to stay on for a second week, but has changed her mind and hands me their air tickets to get altered. (Won't do anything yet: see how it goes). Colonel Horsman stands by saying nothing.

Monday: St Hilarion Castle and Nicosia

All grumbling about early start, dismal breakfast and hot sunshine. Dr Briggs wants to change her room. Must have a room facing west so she can enjoy the evening sun while resting. Had told our company this and even telephoned to remind them. Not pleased. Mrs Horsman asks how I came by such a cushy job – she could easily do it.

It's a short distance to the Crusader castle of St Hilarion, built in the twelfth century and used as a Turkish stronghold after independence. It guards one of the passes through the Kyrenia mountains – a romantic ruin with the original Byzantine walls still more-or-less intact, looking stark and dramatic since a recent forest fire burnt all the vegetation.

We prepare to climb. Hats on, sticks out. Dr Briggs is at the fore, and there is huffing and puffing all round. I wait for the inevitable remark: "How on earth did they get the stones up here? It makes you think."

Mr Faber-Jones whispers that his overweight wife has a heart complaint and shouldn't have come, but please don't say anything. She is wearing a sleeveless cotton dress, her white arms bulging and a small white hat above her round puffy face. He is tall and thin with good features, but looking grey and rather tired. He has forgotten to bring a hat so is wearing his handkerchief knotted at four corners.

Osman, our guide, takes us through the lower part of the castle that was used as stables and up to the main gatehouse – a huge powerful structure originally closed by a drawbridge. Here is the Byzantine chapel and the original refectory, now a bar. Several people, including Osman stop for a drink, while the rest climb further up to the royal apartments. Scaffolding poles act as hand-rails all the way up the steps and at the top we take it in turns to be photographed sitting by the Queen's window, a Gothic opening with remains of tracery with a stone seat below it.

Mr Innes, always ready to educate us, says it was here that Helena Palaeologus, one of the queens of Cyprus, bit off the nose of her husband's mistress in a fit of jealousy.

Colonel Horsman is shocked by some graffiti carved on a rock. '1 RGJ'. "My regiment," he says, disgusted. He has found the climb difficult, but needs a break from his wife who has been complaining non-stop.

"These stones speak to me," says Helen Innes, a gypsy-like figure with long dark hair bundled under a home-made turban which keeps falling apart, and a dirndl skirt almost covering hairy white legs. After she heard about our trip to Turkey in May, she has come to keep an eye on her husband.

I drag Osman and the others out of the bar and back to the bus: everyone wants the loo and queues up for the one working lavatory.

And now we head for Nicosia, the capital of the island – sliced in half by the Green Line which divides Greek from Turkish territory. We shoot along the fast open road – built with Saudi Arabian money. There isn't any shade and the tarmac glistens in the sun, while the original tree-lined track winds romantically round the mountain range below us.

We decamp outside the city walls and walk along the narrow pavement in a disorganised crocodile. Some stop and take photographs, some dive into shops and some nearly dive under cars which have no regard for elderly pedestrians.

Osman leads the way and I stay at the back rounding up the stragglers. The Horsmans (well into their eighties) complain that everyone else is walking too slowly. Dr Briggs has given up the competition and now drags well behind. It's lucky I've been here before and know the way, otherwise we could never catch up with the others along these narrow, overcrowded streets.

The Seliminye Mosque is about to close for a funeral service. Several open coffins are lined up under the porch which most of the party pass with their eyes shut. Dum and Dee have already had enough culture for one day and head off to a bar.

The rest of us have a quick look at the mosque. It was built as the cathedral of St Sophia in the thirteenth century and thanks to the stability of its flying buttresses has survived several earthquakes over the centuries. When the Ottomans invaded in 1571 it became a mosque with two minarets added onto the towers at the west end.

Back at the hotel Mrs Horsman is having second thoughts about going home early. Won't stay in this awful hotel though. Wants to move to the famous Dome Hotel where they have eggs and bacon for breakfast, not cheese, cucumbers, olives and tomatoes. I walk with them through the town and ask the receptionist to show us the bedrooms and dining room. The Colonel notices a sign saying CASINO in large letters. That does it. They will stay put.

Tuesday: Famagusta, Salamis and Bellapais Abbey

A long drive to Famagusta with our driver Abdullah – young, slim, bearded and silent. We always say the driver is the most important person on a tour, and Abdullah rattles along precipitous roads and swings round hairpin bends at speed with complete confidence.

Famagusta was originally a Byzantine fishing port, but when the Crusaders lost their last foothold in the Holy Land, Christian merchants fled here bringing with them untold riches, and set about trading.

Here they built three hundred churches topped by St Nicholas's Cathedral which dominates the main square, and is now of course a mosque. Still its fan-vaulted ceiling and solid pillars remind us of the great Gothic cathedrals at home. In a corner of the north aisle is the tomb of an early bishop depicted holding his staff, with a Latin inscription above him. He is believed to have died from a chill caught while swimming.

The whole city is dusty and dilapidated and you need a lot of imagination to enjoy it, so Dum and Dee, who now know the form, go straight to a bar with Osman. The rest of us wander round the insalubrious market (since closed on account of rats). There is a faded poster of George V and Queen Mary in coronation robes hanging on a wall, and next to it the engagement photograph of Prince Charles and Lady Diana Spencer in that famous blue outfit. Everyone wants to buy cheap saffron and won't believe me when I tell them it is actually turmeric.

We amble through the town to the citadel by the harbour. Here Osman, slightly refreshed by a couple of drinks, tells us that this is Othello's tower, since the play is said to be set in Cyprus at a time when Cyprus was ruled by the Venetians, based on a story of a soldier known as Il Moro.

We climb up steps to the battlements with a view over the harbour, and after Osman has given his spiel Mr Innes steps forwards and recites Elroy Flecker's *The Old Ships,* "dipping deep for Famagusta and the hidden sun that rings black Cyprus with a lake of fire," but he is upstaged by Mr Faber-Jones who, with flamboyant gestures towards the sea, sings snatches from Verdi's opera *Otello.* "Una vela e l'alata leoni!"

In 1570 the Turks landed and headed for Famagusta. After a ten-month siege the Venetians surrendered with an agreement that they would be sent home. The terms were not kept and their general, Bragadino, was flayed alive and stuffed with straw. His remains were later taken to Venice where they now reside in a marble urn in the church of Sts. Giovanni and Paolo.

We carry on to Salamis, the original Roman capital of Cyprus, largely destroyed by an earthquake in the fourth century, rebuilt by the Emperor Constantine, and continued to flourish till it was sacked by Arab raiders three hundred years later.

Most of the town – the size of Eastbourne – is under sand and scrub, still unexcavated, but there is a well-worn tourist trail through the theatre, gymnasium and baths ending up at the communal lavatories: always a star feature with tourists. Cameras out.

Lunch in a shabby restaurant by the sea. It's the only restaurant for miles around – one of the best sites on the island, and it is packed, but the owner Mr Bedi, a lugubrious fellow with a huge red nose, complains that business is bad. The menu hasn't changed for years. Spaghetti, chicken stew or omelettes. Most people opt for omelettes, and they run out of eggs, so one of the waiters is sent off to a nearby farm to get more.

On our way back we stop at Bellapais, the village made famous by Lawrence Durrell's book, *Bitter Lemons*. His house is tastelessly restored and not worth the steep walk up to it (as Mr Innes complained).

We have drinks outside a small bar which doubles as a barber's shop, where inside a man is being shaved with a cut-throat razor and outside stands a familiar red telephone box reminding us of home. Old men sit quietly playing backgammon under a mulberry tree and we explore the tourist shops across the square.

But the glory of Bellapais is its Abbey. It was built on solid bedrock by Augustinian canons fleeing Palestine after 1200, and from below looks more like a fortress than a monastery. As the years passed it fell into moral turpitude – the monks had their concubines, and accepted only their own children as novices.

After the Ottoman invasion it became the romantic ruin we now see. Gothic cloisters lead to the huge refectory with its roof still intact and stone steps lead up to a pulpit where the Abbot read to the monks during meals.

Rider-Haggard visited in 1906 and wrote that the view from the window above the pulpit was the most beautiful and peaceful in the Mediterranean. No longer. Beneath the Abbey is a new hotel with a bright blue swimming pool staring brashly out of an olive grove. Rows and rows of houses – stark white with orange-tiled roofs stretch down to the sea. Mozart's *Eine Kleine Nacht Musik* blares out from the restaurant inside the Abbey grounds.

Mr Innes, still feeling upstaged by Mr Faber-Jones's operatic rendering in Famagusta, invites us to the bar this evening to listen to his cassette of *Otello*. We sit round with drinks while he fiddles with the tape machine. He stands up, arms outstretched, ready to conduct. But instead of a dramatic Placido Domingo, it is the seductive voice of "Hutch" singing *These Foolish Things Remind Me of You*.

Mr Innes indeed feels foolish and blames the tape machine, while the rest of us try not to laugh.

Wednesday: Vouni and Soli

Mr Faber-Jones says his watch has been stolen. He has searched his room and been through the cupboards, but there is no sign of it. I say that if we go to the Police station to report it he will have to miss today's tour, so he decides not to.

Another long drive, but prettier than yesterday as we go westwards through orange groves to the ancient ruins of Vouni.

This was originally a Persian palace, but there are only the foundations left and it's really the view we go for. New crash barriers have been erected on a corner beside a precipitous cliff edge, but unfortunately they have made the bend too tight for our coach so we have to walk the half mile up to the palace. Some want to walk up through the scrub, but change their minds when I tell them that a woman was recently bitten by a snake and nearly lost her leg.

Dum and Dee decide not to come, and sit on a rickety bench with no shade, let alone a bar, while the rest of us start to walk up the steep road. Luckily a car appears and I flag it down and bundle the less able walkers into it before they or the driver can object. We walk round the ruins admiring the view along the northern coast on one side and the distant Troodos Mountains on the other.

Next is Soli, another Roman site with a much-restored theatre ("These stones don't speak to me," says Helen Innes), and the remains of a basilica below it covered with a hideous aluminium hanger. There are beautiful mosaics underneath, but they are crumbling, and pieces are being stolen by unscrupulous tourists.

We have lunch in Guzelyurt in a most unattractive-looking restaurant beside the main road, but the food is good. There is a reproduction of Titian's *Venetian Warrior* on the wall, and I wonder if the restaurant owner sees the irony in this.

Then, to the museum over the road. Natural history is on the ground floor – an extraordinary collection. Fish, in one glass case, have faded to a pale yellow, while birds in another look moth-eaten having lost most of their feathers. A pelican has a long piece of sticking plaster ineptly wrapped round its neck, with a fish, similarly wrapped, in its beak. There is also a freaks' case. A lamb with five legs, a fox with two heads and a hen with three feet. "Gives me the creeps," says Mrs Horsman.

The church next door is dedicated to St Mamas – the patron saint of tax dodgers; Osman tells us the story. The saint refused to pay his taxes and was hauled up before the Byzantine emperor. He trotted into court astride a lion that he had tamed on the way and was excused paying taxes for life. "Good for him," they all say.

We drive back on a road south of the Kyrenia range. Here, on the flat plain, in the middle of nowhere are brand new buildings: night clubs. "Lipstick Lady," "Sexy Squirrel." Who on earth goes to them we wonder?

Our driver, Abdullah, suddenly stops the bus, gets out and dives under a scrubby bush. He comes back with four partridge chicks in his hands and puts them on the floor of the bus. They run all over the place cheeping desperately and we are shocked when Abdullah says he is going to keep them in a cage.

I notice Mr Faber-Jones is wearing his watch at dinner. He doesn't say anything and nor do I.

Thursday: Shipwreck

Our last day. A boat trip suggested on the written itinerary sent out to clients has aroused a lot of interest, but Osman has been warning everyone against it. Although the sea looks flat there is a terrific swell. "The more you try and put us off, the more we want to go," says Helen Innes.

Mrs Briggs decides to go scuba diving and the Horsmans are wisely staying behind. The rest of us walk to the harbour.

We pass handsome, newly varnished boats all ready for boarding with smiling crews in smart uniforms, and stop at a bedraggled-looking vessel called *The Cyprus Belle* that has seen better days.

There are already two dingy-looking English couples sprawled across the seats in the stern, not moving to let us pass. One man has a greasy, grey pony tail tied with a bit of string and one of the women is wearing a pink tee shirt with "I love Greece" across it. Not very tactful in these parts. My genteel little group looks a bit disapproving, and Osman has a row with the captain as we had booked the boat for ourselves only.

Lunch is brought aboard in black plastic sacks and we set sail. There is very little space to sit and some stay in the cockpit at the stern under cover, breathing diesel fumes, while others lie uncomfortably on the roof of the cabin under a furled sail.

As soon as we are out of the harbour and on the open sea they begin to feel sick and hang on to anything they can grab as the boat rolls from side to side. It's an incredibly boring voyage along the unlovely built-up coast. Chug, chug, chug, very slowly.

Everybody is feeling dreadful and I dole out plastic bags. I have a slim volume of Palgrave's *Golden Treasury of Love Poems* in my pocket and flip through them. "I wish I were where Helen lies." I certainly don't. Helen Innes is lying on her side clutching a handkerchief with a plastic bag at the ready, while Mrs Faber-Jones is holding her arm to make sure she doesn't slide off the cabin roof. Dum and Dee are hanging on to each other so they don't roll into the water.

Osman says we will have lunch in a beautiful bay, but when we get there it is much too rough to drop anchor, so we turn round and head back.

The captain is looking anxious and opens the hatch-cover on the lower deck. A huge fountain of oil and water spurts out over everyone and the mate goes down into the hatch and tries to stem the flow. Water and oil everywhere.

Shouting and panicking. Osman makes frantic calls on his mobile.

We head towards a little harbour which is in army territory, and sit in its calmer waters, but the anchor doesn't hold so we drift around.

The bay, once the harbour of the ancient Greek city of Lambousa, is now a private beach for army families who stand staring at us while soldiers on the cliff above look threatening with rifles at the ready. Below the cliff is a restaurant with a large sign saying CAMELOT. So now we know where Camelot really is. Back to Palgrave.

> "The shallop flitteth silken-sail'd
> Skimming down to Camelot."

Not quite us....our "shallop" is sinking slowly, but most of the passengers are feeling too ill to notice.

Suddenly a speed-boat appears from nowhere and circles round soaking us with its wash.

Rescue. It is a lifeboat, crewed by sailors from the Turkish navy. It draws up beside us and begins the difficult task of getting our lot aboard – both boats heaving up and down and passengers in no condition to leap over the gap between us.

Dum and Dee, both dead weights, are carried across with difficulty and others rely on strong-armed rescuers to heave them over. What a contrast between the sailors in their neat, buff-coloured uniforms and our motley lot who have lost all dignity and look grubby and dishevelled.

We have an exciting journey back to Kyrenia for anyone not feeling sea-sick, bumping over waves at high speed with 12ft-high wash behind. We disembark into a waiting bus – I can't help noticing a grin on the driver's face – and drive to our hotel. Everyone recovers quickly and is soon tucking into a late lunch, where from the dining room window we can see the dismal sight of *The Cyprus Belle*, nearly under water, being towed slowly back to harbour.

Friday

The Horsmans are up at the crack of dawn to see us off. They are very happy to be staying on for another week.

"I've only got one criticism of this holiday," Mr Faber-Jones writes in a letter to our tour company, "That boat was not seaworthy."

Egypt
Sands of the Nile

~ November ~

Cast List

Lord and Lady Gilliat	*Newly appointed life peer and down-trodden wife*
Mr and Mrs Tallboy	*Assertive couple: still not used to group travel*
Mr and Mrs Barnes	*Laid-back husband with socially-aware wife*
Engaged Couple	*About to embark on second marriages*
Mrs Deeprose	*Sensible widow who gets on with everyone*
Miss Mollard	*Mouse who doesn't want to be a nuisance*
And others	

Ancient Egypt must have been a serene place – surrounded by deserts and seas, ruled for twenty five centuries by its own kings, with no close neighbours and very few invasions and wars. Not that the people were calm – DNA shows that the ancient Egyptians were exactly the same people as modern ones, and Egypt is not a calm place – noisy, grubby, exciting, usually friendly but always hectic. It is the longest, thinnest country in the world (after Chile) – a tiny strip of cultivation as wide as the Nile can be induced to flood, stretching between endless deserts.

Tuesday: London – Cairo

A civilised time to leave Heathrow: four o'clock in the afternoon. The clients arrive in dribs and drabs, with the Gilliats appearing last with five pieces of luggage. "Did you pack your own bags?" asks the check-in girl uninterestedly. "No, our housekeeper did." The check-in girl looks up startled, then notices their passports in ostentatious House of Lord's folders. Lord G. is obviously enjoying his recent elevation. He is large and authoritative, wearing a tweed suit and a check shirt and of course a tie. His thinning grey hair is neatly smoothed down with Trumper's Extract of Limes. His wife is tiny, with a snub nose and fluffy hair, and keeps very close to him. She is, I guess, the sort of woman who has never had to make decisions or take any responsibility.

The flight arrives early and we are met by Medhat the agent. I have told everybody that we are Fast Track – our passports will be whipped away and we will be swept through immigration. No such luck. We are Slow Track, and one by one we edge forward in a long queue. Medhat tells us to wait while he collects the luggage – which takes ages because five pieces are missing. Everyone identifies their own bags except Lord Gilliat who is sitting with his wife well apart from the rest of us. The lost luggage is found: Gilliats' of course. There are huge red labels with Lord Gilliat in huge black letters, but none of our company's labels which Medhat has been looking out for.

All the other tourists have gone and the baggage hall is empty with no porters in sight, so Medhat and his assistant pile up the bags and take them to the waiting bus. Very efficiently, he has all the room keys, or rather cards, ready to hand out, and soon we are at our grand, bland American hotel.

Everyone goes straight up to their rooms and come straight down again. Someone is sleeping in their beds. Goldilocks? The rooms are re-allocated, but where on earth is the luggage? The porters are incredibly slow and people keep wandering down looking for their bags. It's disgraceful and I blow up poor Medhat, whose fault it isn't. Three-quarters of an hour later all the bags have arrived and by half past one we are in bed. I've known worse.

Wednesday: Cairo

I am woken by the television. "Good morning Mrs Taylor" flashes across the screen accompanied by soft music. I look at my watch – 5.30am. I doze angrily for another couple of hours, then go down to meet guide Fatima and run through programme.

She is a handsome, heavily built woman with dark hair and flashing eyes, and I realise immediately that she is going to talk too much. "The itinerary is too tight," she says. "We should leave at eight o'clock."

We leave at nine. Some are late. Mrs Barnes says she thought this was meant to be a holiday, and the Tallboys say they hate being bossed around. They came with me to Jordan in March, and I am surprised to see them again. They have been to Egypt before so know everything. She is big and bossy with reddish dyed hair swept back into an Alice band; he is swarthy and smooth, and reminds me of Rex Mottram in *Brideshead*.

The Gilliats are on time, looking disapprovingly at latecomers. Everyone had an unwelcome television awakening at 5.30 and Mrs Deeprose and Miss Mollard (complete strangers until last night) were given an enormous suite after the Goldilocks incident, but only one bed.

Off we go – to Dahshur we think – but Fatima suddenly switches the itinerary and we head for Giza and the pyramids.

Once they were reached by a pleasant tree-lined avenue, but this has become a seemingly endless road of uncontrolled ribbon development and it is a shock to find that the pyramids are in a suburb of Cairo. A bit disappointing really. Their size is astonishing – but we have all seen vast buildings before, and they seem hardly more human than Mont Blanc. There are three of them – the sole survivors of the Seven Wonders of the ancient world – built nearly five thousand years ago for succeeding Pharaohs. Originally they were encased in white polished limestone, but in the nineteenth century Egyptian builders stripped the casing for their own use, leaving the softer stones exposed to the elements. Until recently daring tourists (including Florence Nightingale) would climb up the outside of the pyramids, but Health and Safety has spread its tentacles as far as here and it is now forbidden.

The stronger members of the party follow Fatima inside. It is claustrophobic and rather smelly. "Reminds me of our old air-raid shelter," whispers Miss Mollard, a nervous twitching woman, trailing behind her confident, extrovert bed-mate, Mrs Deeprose.

We walk up a dark, narrow passage with a low roof, first into the Queen's chamber, then the King's. Fatima explains, at great length, that the pyramid was the means by which the dead pharaoh rose to the firmament and joined the sun. We are glad to get out and join the sun ourselves, and have free time to go for a camel ride or visit the Solar Boat Museum. The boat displayed here was unearthed in 1954 – a cedar wood vessel that is now displayed in an unprepossessing modern building to the south of the pyramids. It is believed to have been used to bring the bodies of pharaohs down the Nile. Meanwhile the camel party have a trickier time. When you mount a camel it kneels down to let you get on, and then it jerks up, tossing you into mid-air if you don't hang on tightly.

Back on the bus, with the Barneses just in time, but there is no sign of the Tallboys. They appear ten minutes later, having been looking unsuccessfully for shops. I glare ostentatiously at my watch, but no apologies are forthcoming.

We go and see the Sphinx. This looks enormous in all the eighteenth century prints, but in fact it's quite small and you look down on it sitting in a sand pit – rather undignified with its broken nose.

Bill Barnes has started singing an unsuitable ditty to the tune of *The Eton Boating Song* about the sexual life of the Sphinx. His wife scowls, so he hums instead. He is a retired land-agent with a red face and an easy smile; remarkably tolerant of his rather silly wife who name-drops endlessly.

Fatima takes us to a papyrus showroom. The papyrus here is expensive, but it rolls up easily, meaning it is probably real papyrus and not banana leaves. Some buy and some don't.

Off to Dahshur for more pyramids. Until recently this was a restricted military zone and has been opened so recently that touts and camel drivers haven't yet colonised it. There is a nest of pyramids here, but only the Bent and the Red (the oldest of all the pyramids) are intact. We go down 125 stone steps into the bowels of the interior. Fatima gives us an interminable lecture on dynasties, then we have lots of free time to wander round – more perhaps than we actually wanted. There is no hurry.

Back on the bus we head for Sakkara. Fatima suddenly announces that the site closes at 4.00pm and it is now 3.55. It closes as we arrive, and everyone is annoyed, so Fatima reminds us that we should have started at 8am – but now, very luckily, there is time for us to visit a carpet shop.

We are back by early evening and everybody is whacked. Some have dinner in the hotel coffee shop, others stay in their rooms which are now full of flowers, baskets of fruit and chocolates in the shape of pyramids (an apology from management for rotten porterage, Goldilocks rooms and television alarm calls).

I visit Mrs Deeprose and Miss Mollard who are quite happy in their double bed as long as the others don't think they are lesbians. Then I remind everybody to bring their air tickets down in the morning to confirm return flights to England. Very important.

Thursday: Cairo

Five o'clock alarm call for those going to the camel market at Birqash – about twenty miles north-west of Cairo. We set off with Medhat, clutching breakfast boxes. There are no other tourists and it is definitely not for animal lovers or the faint-hearted. Hundreds of camels are sold here every day. Most of them have come from western Sudan and have been herded together in trucks for the last two days of the journey, but some are so emaciated that they are only good for the knacker's yard.

There is hustle and bustle, shouting and fighting – we are back in biblical times. The stink is overwhelming. Most camels have one leg doubled up and tied so they can't run away, but one lot haven't and suddenly stampede. We dodge, first the camels, then the traders wielding sticks and beating them mercilessly. Mrs Deeprose tries to tell them off and Miss Mollard is in tears.

We return by nine o'clock, and everybody hands over their air tickets except the Engaged Couple who have lost theirs.

We walk through a shopping arcade to the Egyptian museum, which stands beside the bus station at the side of a busy square. The fumes from the traffic go straight through the open windows, so it is no wonder that a new museum is being built outside the city centre.

The present building is nearly a hundred years old and far too small for its vast collection of antiquities which have never been reorganised. But there is a certain charm in the old-fashioned glass cases standing on tall legs, and the atmosphere of museum mustiness which will surely be lost in brand new surroundings.

We all go to the Tutankhamun Galleries where most are soon exhausted by Fatima's non-stop commentary, and wander off on their own.

O.K. BUT DO NOT BE LATE FOR THE BUS.

It's time to go. And the Barneses are just in time, but one couple is missing. The bus driver is frantic because he isn't allowed to wait here and hoots his horn repeatedly.

The Missing Persons (Tallboys of course) drift into sight. "Sorry we're late." They aren't a bit.

Lunch is in a restaurant in a bazaar. The Engaged Couple, rather snappy over lost tickets, are each blaming the other, wedding bells hanging by a thread. The Gilliats bump into old friends – a well-dressed youngish couple (isn't it a small world?) "That's the fifth richest woman in England," hisses Mrs Barnes, who knows about these things.

We go on to the Citadel and visit a nineteenth century mosque, built by the Khedive Mohamed Ali – vast and grand. I would much rather have seen the Suleyman Pasha mosque – four hundred years older and far more beautiful, but the tour company has dictated otherwise. Instead Fatima frog-marches us back to Sakkara, which this time is open. Here is the stepped pyramid, the ancestor of all pyramids and indeed of all grand stone monuments. It was designed for the Pharaoh by his doctor, a man called Imhotep who later got worshipped as a god – rather irritating for the Pharaoh, if he ever found out. Thank goodness the pyramid is open. No flash photography is allowed in the tomb – but the custodian turns a blind eye if given a large tip.

We have dinner in the restaurant on the roof of the hotel overlooking the Nile with wonderful views over Cairo. NO CHARGE. It is laid on by the management – a second apology for rotten porterage, Goldilocks rooms and television alarm calls.

Friday: Cairo — Abu Simbel — Aswan

Four o'clock alarm call. The Gilliats appear at breakfast appealing for luggage straps as the zip has broken on one of their suitcases. Mrs Deeprose, very practical, suggests putting the case in a large plastic bag. One of the waiters disappears and comes back smiling, with an enormous thick, black plastic bag. A body bag – perfect, hotels always have a good supply. The suitcase is popped in, tied up with string and off we all go to the airport. (The porters at the hotel, hoping for a tip, couldn't be more helpful).

We drop off Medhat and the Engaged Couple at the international airport to get replacement tickets, while the rest of party carry on to Domestic Departures for the flight to Aswan.

"Passports are not needed but keep them with you," says Fatima. Oh dear, the Gilliats have packed theirs, but in which of their five suitcases? Once in the airport they start to go through their bags, leaving the body bag till last. Then they undo the string, take out the suitcase, undo the luggage straps and start taking things out. There is no sign, so they dig deeper and lay all their garments out on chairs. Still no sign and the contents of the suitcases are scattered round the departure lounge which is becoming crowded with interested spectators. There is still no sign and he suggests she looks in her hand-bag. "I've LOOKED," she shouts. He furiously tips her bag upside down, and the large ostentatious passports fall out. He turns purple, but says nothing. Nor does she.

The Engaged Couple appear with new tickets, hand in hand, looking happier, but the rest of party is getting unhappier as time goes by and nothing happens. There are grumbles about having to get up so early. All other flights are called and we sit still. "Fog," they say. Any excuse.

Eventually we board a tiny plane and fly to Aswan. The Engaged Couple and I get off and go straight on the boat for a late afternoon lunch. Others fly on to Abu Simbel for the afternoon. It is a great success, especially as guides are not allowed to talk inside the temple.

Everybody is pleased with the boat, which is much smaller that the huge liners in which most tourists are travelling. It just holds our party of twenty-five, but the cabins are very cramped and the Barnses ask to change because theirs smells of diesel fumes.

Still, no time to waste, and we are off in a felucca around Lord Kitchener's Island. Boatmen bring out beaded necklaces and bracelets to sell while a waiter serves us tea. Little boys, hoping for tips, row round the felucca in little boats singing "Row, row, row your boat........"

Back on our boat, the manager suggests a show on board tonight. I say NO. Captain's drinks party and early bed.

Saturday: Aswan – Philae Island

Lord Gilliat is complaining bitterly about going to Aswan High Dam and the granite quarries (supported by little yaps from his wife). They and the Tallboys have seen them before so they shouldn't be on programme. Could they be dropped off somewhere? No way.

Fatima has altered the programme again – no Edfu today. Mrs Barnes says she wants time to sit on the boat; not all this rush. Fatima says she has never known such an undisciplined group. "They never listen," she says. "You talk too much," I say.

First we see the sights of Aswan – a charming sea-side town, except the 'sea' is the river. We are on the Tropic of Cancer, and it is much warmer than Cairo, though still a pleasant heat. We pass the Low Dam which the British built, and which was never quite high enough to control the flow of the Nile. Above it is the enormous High Dam, which Nasser persuaded the Russians to build after Suez. It did its job, but at the cost of drowning the ancient and beautiful province of Nubia, the most southerly part of Egypt. Abu Simbel was physically moved up the cliff, and though its site is impressive it's not authentic. The Gilliats and Tallboys don't get off the bus but sit there scowling, to avoid polluting their eyes with anything they'd seen already.

At the granite quarries, we are amazed by the skill with which huge pillars like Cleopatra's needle were carved from the rock. "It makes you think," said Mrs Barnes. "That'll be a first," says Mrs Tallboy, cattily, behind her hand.

Gilliats delighted to bump into the fifth richest woman in England again and stand still, chatting until it is time to go.

Everybody loves Philae Island (it's not really Philae, which was flooded when the High Dam was built, and the temples all moved to another island), but it is still a beautiful open site, dominated by the temple of Isis.

Because Fatima has changed the itinerary, the crowds are all leaving and we have the place almost to ourselves, but, unlike Florence Nightingale who spent five days here in 1842, we whizz round in order to make time for shopping at the stalls by the jetty. Some of them are run by Nubians – famous, Fatima says, for their physical beauty. They are indeed handsome, and much more restrained than the Egyptians in chasing customers. Some clients buy galabeyas – the nightdress-like garment worn by Egyptian villagers – for the party tonight. Poor Miss Mollard, not used to bargaining, pays an astronomical price for her outfit and is very upset.

Most people are dreading the party which is laid on by the manager of the boat and is obligatory for all cruises. "This isn't a Butlin's holiday," says Mrs Tallboy.

I had wondered if we could cancel it, but one or two people have brought out clothes from England and are looking forward to showing them off.

When it comes to it, everyone enters into the spirit, and even those who haven't bought clothes improvise with anything they can find in their cabins. There is dancing and one or two silly games.

Sunday: Edfu – Esna – Luxor

An eight o'clock start – we are to travel by horse and carriage to the temple at Edfu. Every boatload of tourists disembarks at the same moment and there is chaos, with horses rearing, drivers yelling and clients bewildered. Each carriage has a number which has to be memorised, to make sure that you come back in the same one and, most importantly, tip the right coachman.

The temple when we get there is jam-packed with tourists. It is the Temple of Horus, the falcon-headed god. Most impressive, and hardly damaged, is the great gateway – shaped like two wedges of cheese pointing upwards, with a vast doorway between. All the guides are shouting at once, but luckily Fatima has the loudest voice of all.

Inside the temple there is a tourist (not us) behind every pillar being sick. It is so squalid. We can't enjoy this visit and try to find our carriages for the return journey – more chaos. Clients tip generously but no thanks from graceless drivers.

We sail down the river, and there is at last time to sit on deck and sunbathe. Some change into shorts, and Bill Barnes adds a colonial touch with long shorts, knee-length stockings and garters with little green tabs.

We dock at Esna and visit the Roman temple of the ram god – Khnum. What survives is a great hall of pillars, decorated with coloured reliefs. Afterwards, by request, Fatima takes us through little back streets to visit a Coptic Christian church. On the way we watch an old man in a barber's shop sitting in the doorway ironing; he sucks a sponge and spits onto the garment. A world away from England we think, until Bill Barnes points to a large faded reproduction of Constable's *Hay Wain* on the wall behind the barber's head.

The church is tiny and half-ruined, with a hole in the roof. It is packed with children attending a service, and on the way out we are greeted by two men in galabeyas, who pull up their sleeves to show us the little blue Coptic crosses tattooed on their wrists. We stuff the church's collecting box with large notes.

Back to the boat and more free time, with two fours of bridge. We have made a few changes to the programme and won't have such an early start in the morning. Everyone is pleased, except of course Lord Gilliat: "I wanted the programme as it was – and why did we have to visit the high dam at Aswan?" I take a few deep breaths and say nothing.

The Tallboys aren't coming back with us at the end of the tour, but are flying on to South Africa. I remind them to give me their air-tickets tonight for reconfirmation in the morning.

Monday: Luxor and Valley of Kings

From here onwards, I begin to get rather a different prospective of Fatima. In Cairo she had been noisy, bullying and manipulative, herding us into shops that would pay her a commission. Now she shows herself genuinely knowledgeable and helpful, changing the programme to visit temples and tombs when they were likely to be emptier.

Everyone has a long lie-in except the Tallboys who had forgotten to give me their tickets, and of course the agent came at dawn to collect them. The Engaged Couple are going on a private tour of the sites, as they are off too, flying to Mauritius later today. We say goodbye to them and wish them long happiness and no more lost tickets.

We have an early lunch and then off to the Valley of the Kings – the royal necropolis. Everyone swoops on copies of *The Times* and *Telegraph* on sale outside the entrance.

Our timing is good since the crowds are leaving the site, and we have excellent viewing of Queen Hatshepsut's vast temple with its background of high red cliffs. She was an interesting lady – not a consort or a regent, but a female Pharaoh, god-king and all – her statues even show her with a beard. Miss Mollard touches my arm. She has suddenly remembered that she has left three silk shirts in the hotel at Cairo and is very worried. Please could I possibly get them back?

We pass on to the tombs, first the royal ones, spacious underground chambers, well-lit now and so beautifully decorated that one could spend one's life there, let alone one's after-life. Next to the ticket office there is another sort of memorial – a posh shop selling alabaster statuettes of Princess Diana. Strange, these funerary customs.

Back on board I am horrified to see the Engaged Couple lolling on the deck. They should have caught their plane ages ago. Lost tickets? No, their flight was cancelled and they are getting later one. Phew!

We have an orgy tonight – belly-dancers. People are happy chatting, and annoyed that they have to leave the dining room in the middle of dinner to go and watch them. However, in the lounge we find our pudding – meringue models of the pyramids, and a chocolate sphinx with cherries for eyes looking like Thomas the Tank Engine. The belly show is awful with ghastly loud music and some of the audience are forced to join in a sort of conga. "Belly dancing," said Bill Barnes sagely "is not what it was. All the great performers have retired, no-one can be bothered to learn the ancient skills, and if you want a real show you'd do better to go to a little club I know behind the Edgware Road."

But on the stroke of nine the entertainers pack up and rush off to their next engagement. I give the Tallboys their tickets and tell them (jokingly) not to lose them.

Tuesday: Luxor – Karnak

We are on parade with our luggage at eight o'clock – all sorry to be leaving the boat with its friendly staff, but we are staying in a hotel for the last two nights. First though the temple of Amun-Re at Karnak – a processional way leading to its huge gates, guarded by ram-headed sphinxes. This was the "centre of the world" where Amun, creator of the universe first created himself and then all living things. Beyond the gates is a courtyard full of columns nearly a hundred feet high, like god-sized cricket stumps. Although the roof has long gone, the height and density of the pillars preserves the sense of mystery, for it was here, in the inner sanctuary, that the solemn rites were celebrated, which kept Egypt and the universe in their place.

Lord Gilliat looks at his watch and announces that is eleven o'clock on November 11th so we must keep two minutes silence. We stand self-consciously in a group, eyes tightly shut, thinking not about the Fallen I am afraid, but how ridiculous we must look to the crowds surrounding us. We are relieved when Fatima's voice breaks the silence and orders us to the bus.

The Winter Palace is a lovely old-fashioned hotel, with wide corridors and large rooms – perhaps a little the worse for wear – but it has great charm.

We are in the new wing – the comfortable, modern rooms, entirely lacking in character. It's lovely to have some space though, after the cramped cabins on the boat. The mini-bars aren't working. "It's a long story," says the hotel manager.

An early dinner for those going to the Sound and Light show at Karnak in the huge soulless dining room which is almost empty. The Sound and Light show, by contrast, is a Hollywood-type extravaganza. We join the crowds and walk up the avenue of sphinxes, through the great court and on to the grandstand beside the sacred lake for the show's finale. The loud music and dramatic text recounting the history of ancient Thebes are well over the top, but it is worth it just to walk through this temple at night.

Wednesday: Luxor

It's a free day and some of the party want to go bird-watching. Miss Mollard is uncertain whether to go until she sees the good-looking English guide. Most of the party lie by the pool, including Mrs Barnes who has found a two-day old copy of the *Daily Mail,* but one or two go and explore Luxor, and the Tallboys pay an exorbitant price to go on a private tour of the Valley of the Kings with Fatima.

After lunch some go to inspect the Sheraton Hotel where they were hoping we were going to stay, and return greatly relieved we aren't.

Mrs Deeprose (who is game for anything), and I hire rickety bikes, cross the Nile on a ferry and revisit the West Bank. We have the whole site to ourselves with not another tourist in sight.

Tonight Fatima has wangled us into the dining room at the Old Winter Palace, at no extra charge. It has a lovely atmosphere and scrumptious food, and best of all, several friends from England are spotted at tables across the room. Small World.

Thursday: Luxor – Heathrow

Quarter-to-five call. It's pitch dark and the lights aren't working. The fire alarm goes off and everyone ignores it. At least the lifts are working, and off we go, accompanied by Medhat, to the airport. It is chaotic. There are no porters and people grab bags and lug them to the check-in. My mobile rings. It is an irate Mr Tallboy trying to leave the hotel to catch the flight to South Africa.

"You have our tickets," he says accusingly.

"YOU HAVE THEM. LOOK IN YOUR BAGS."

Here at the check-in there is a fierce argument between Medhat and the man behind the desk. The clients go quiet and look uneasy. Perhaps we aren't booked on the flight? My mobile rings again. It's the Tallboys, who still can't find their tickets. Surely, surely, surely I gave them back to them? I can't do anything now. Medhat disappears and I am left trying to sort out the check-in, wishing that everyone wouldn't crowd round me at the desk. Lots of tapping on computers and finally, thank goodness, it is all right and we are on our way. The journey is comfortable, but it's a long flight with Fatima's voice still ringing in our ears.

As for Tallboys: I hear when I get back to the office that they had found the tickets and caught their plane. Apology? Guess.

Ethiopia
The Lost Ark

~ December ~

Cast List

Marge and Chris Graham	*Well-travelled, camera-slung couple*
Virginia Smythe	*Widow 1 from Cheltenham*
John Stafford	*Permanently worried ex-civil servant*
Sarah Barrington-Brown	*Widow 2, earnest, with social conscience.*
Sheila Harris	*Hardly speaks*
Linda Chalmers	*Twelve-stone / five feet-tall, schoolmistress*
Alan and Jean Welleby	*Brother and sister who live together*
Gebre Selassie	*Our guide, known as Gabriel, or the Archangel*
And others	

The tours in Ethiopia were in some ways the hardest I have done. The land is an ancient Christian civilisation, long cut off from Europe by a ring of Islamic countries. At the time I was there it was tragically poor (though it has grown rapidly since then), and conditions for tourists were not easy – especially for the old and frail, however brave.

We followed an itinerary round the ancient cities – a tourist route that is becoming more and more popular as tourism is expanding.

Friday: Heathrow – Addis Ababa

Rather a quiet party at Heathrow. Miss Welleby says she doesn't know why she has come and Miss Chalmers wishes she hadn't. Sheila Harris has had a chest infection for three weeks and is unable to speak. It's a good start.

Miss Welleby starts to nag her brother and cheers up. She is late sixties (they all seem to be), with grey hair and a watery complexion complemented by a beige wind-cheater and beige trousers. Her brother is even more faded – in another beige jacket – his neck muscles hanging loose without a tie to keep them together, and such a far-away look in his eyes that you wonder if he knows where he is. He takes a book out of his bag and ignores his sister.

Miss Chalmers looks as though she ought to be enjoying herself. She is big and bouncy, with a ruddy complexion, and looks more like a farmer's wife than a teacher. Silent Sheila has a pale face under a layer of even paler powder, brightened up by some shiny red lipstick making her look like a rather pathetic clown. The

Grahams, a handsome couple from the north of England, are much more positive. They have deep tans and lots of gold-jangling jewellery, and start recalling holidays that they have already had this year. They interrupt each other and argue so much that they don't realise that nobody is listening.

Saturday: Addis Ababa

Its brilliant sunshine at Addis and "Somewhere Over the Rainbow" is grinding out over a loudspeaker to welcome us. We are met by Gebre our guide, small, dark and quietly spoken with perfect English.

Addis Ababa – its name means New Flower – was founded in the late nineteenth century and claims to be the third highest capital in the world.

Our itinerary says "fine architecture, cosy espresso bars and bustling markets, with the pungent aroma of spicy cooking, form a unique Ethiopian pastiche."

We drive through streets lined with tatty white buildings, swarming with beggars, cripples and street-hawkers, and even Heathrow airport seems luxury by comparison.

The Hilton Hotel is more like home – set in fifteen acres of grounds in the smarter end of Addis – but our tired, untidy little group look out of place in the huge marble entrance hall with white sofas and plate glass windows overlooking extensive gardens.

The check-in takes ages, with a bored receptionist behind the smart mahogany desk, and after a quick wash and an even quicker lunch we set off sightseeing – all except the Cheltenham Widow, Virginia Smythe, who has spent a lot of her life abroad, and settles down beside the swimming pool with a Dick Francis thriller.

We are meant to visit the Africa Hall and the National Museum, but the Africa Hall is permanently closed to the public and shouldn't be on the itinerary. The National Museum contains the famous skull of Lucy – thought to be our oldest ancestor – a girl three million years old who lived half her life in the trees, and died, apparently, from eating too much hyena's liver.

Later, it's welcome drinks for everyone in my bedroom – hoping it's not nicer than theirs. Sometimes I am given a huge suite of rooms; to impress my tour company no doubt, and sometimes a tiny staff bedroom, but usually it is the same nondescript room as everyone else. I have hidden the bowl of rotting fruit and stale cake left for me with the compliments of manager just in case the others are jealous, and have ordered local wine, which is indifferent, but drinkable. Everyone soon perks up.

The hotel looks impressive, but is inefficiently run and I have an argument with a disagreeable manager over the vouchers for breakfast which he is reluctant to give us. It is too late to knock up the clients so I slip the vouchers under their doors, hoping I've got the right rooms.

Sunday: Addis

John Stafford is worried. He is a senior and serious Civil Servant and looks older than he is, with deep lines across his brow shown up by his very short hair cut and deep set eyes. He lives with his mother in London and wonders whether he should be leaving her for so long. He found three packets of coloured condoms on his pillow last night and thought they might be cough sweets, so brings them down to breakfast for inspection.

Off we go to Debre Libanos Monastery, one of the holiest sites in Ethiopia. It is a two hour drive and there are no loos, so we delve into the bushes on arrival.

The present church is modern and plain and uninteresting – sitting in a peaceful wooded gorge, with its derelict thirteenth century predecessor nearby.

We have a picnic lunch under trees with hunks of bread, slices of cheese and oranges, washed down with bottles of fizzy water. Good Enid Blyton stuff.

There are hundreds of baboons with long manes and pink chests swinging from the trees just above us. Their noise and numbers make them terrifying for a moment, but these are the popular gelada baboons which are said to be much less threatening than other species. Miss Chalmers is worried about mosquitoes and takes a bee-keeper's hat, complete with veil, out of an enormous shabby handbag. She looks like Lady Bracknell. Actually, she looks ridiculous.

We walk down to a bridge below us to view the Blue Nile gorge – Ethiopia's answer to the Grand Canyon – two thousand feet deep. Everyone has great difficulty walking the twenty yards back to the bus, puffing and panting and sitting down every few minutes. Jet-lag and altitude has got to them. Silent Sheila is white and gasping: thank goodness no lipstick.

We are flying up to Gonder in the morning and I tell everybody that when they pack tonight they mustn't put any electrical stuff, batteries, lighters, matches or knives in their hand luggage. Worried Civil Servant (Condom John) is very worried because he has heard of at least two planes crashing because there were batteries in the hold.

The Earnest widow with a social conscience has done her homework – read guide-books, been to lectures, supports an Ethiopian charity and has learnt a few words of Amharic. She has a rather breathless, intense voice and persuades the Wellebys to go and have dinner at local restaurant. They eat injera – the staple diet of Ethiopians – grey foam rubber made of fermented grain, shaped into a pancake. You break bits off and dip them into a hot sauce.

Monday: Addis – Bahir Dar – Gonder

Miss Welleby has been violently sick all night. Poor worried John hasn't slept a wink and has decided to defy authority and keep his batteries and lighter in his hand luggage.

I have a row with the hotel manager because he has tried to charge us for breakfast. We set off for the airport, with Miss Welleby feeling dreadful, clutching two enormous plastic laundry bags in case she is sick. The Earnest Widow can't find her air ticket so panics and throws everything out of her suitcase onto the floor of the bus. There is no sign of it, so when we get to the airport we send her back to the hotel with the driver where she finds the ticket on her bed.

There are endless searches and frisks at the airport. Poor Worried John's batteries and lighters are confiscated and his luggage gone through with a fine tooth-comb.

Eventually we reach Bahir Dar, where we are breaking our journey to Gonder for a few hours, at a lovely hotel on edge of Lake Tana. We hope to "hear lake water lapping with low sound by the shore," but "Greensleeves" is belting out over a loudspeaker. Our Cheltenham Widow has ordered a tin of 7-Up and sits in a deck-chair sipping warm Pimms (never travels without it) in a short-sleeved Horrock's cotton frock, while Miss Welleby lies asleep beside her wrapped in two jerseys and a fleece.

After lunch we return to the airport for the flight to Gonder. Miss Welleby looks at death's door, and the Earnest Widow, feeling guilty about last night's dinner, tactlessly asks if she is feeling better.

Camera-slung Marge embarrasses us by losing her temper (in a corn-crake voice) with airport officials when they investigate her battery-charger. We board a seventeen-seater plane and have a bumpy flight to Gonder. Corn-crake is sick twice. Serves her right. It is an even more bumpy drive from the airport to our hotel and Corn-crake is still being sick. Poor thing. Now I feel guilty.

We arrive at the hotel and sit on a terrace drinking wine and watching the sun setting behind the mountains. All the hotels are government owned and run, and built on the same lines with the same characteristics, like centipedes in the lavatory, spiders in the bath and hot water if you are lucky. They all have lovely views and pretty gardens, spoilt by empty, cracked swimming pools in the middle. Cheltenham Widow isn't happy with her room, so I offer to swap and she cheers up, even though the rooms are identical. Some people are worried about mosquitoes, except Lady Bracknell who has brought a mosquito net with her. I'm much more concerned about fleas, remembering past visits here.

Tuesday: Gonder

No complaints about fleas, and I'm glad to see that Lady Bracknell has taken advantage of the cheap laundry, as I've been getting rather tired of her bright orange tee-shirt hanging loose over her large hips. Miss Welleby (ghostly white) appears briefly to say she isn't coming on today's tour, and no one asks if she is feeling better.

It's a two hour drive to Gorgora to see the Debre Sina Maryam church. There is no air-conditioning in the bus, so we travel with the windows open, and try and shut them quickly every time a vehicle, disguised as a sand-storm, approaches. But the windows are difficult to shut, and we often don't make it, so the sand-storm whirls round inside.

We have elevenses at a hotel by the shore of a lake – a beautiful site surrounded by jacaranda trees and hanging curtains of bougainvillea; but it's an uninviting hotel, with broken furniture, cracked china, loos which don't work, and general filth. We walk to the church through the garden between upturned plastic chairs and piles of rubbish. There are seventeenth century frescoes on the walls of the church with all our old friends – Daniel, Jonah, St Stephen dodging a fusillade of buns, and St George (our boy), skewering his dragon. In Ethiopian religious paintings the righteous are painted full face and the evil-doers in profile, and all the characters are white, except the devil.

Back to Gonder, for lunch of "marconi and tomato source," and then on to visit the old city.

Gonder was the capital of Ethiopia for two hundred and fifty years and is very much on the tourist map. The Royal Enclosure is a huge walled space in the middle of the modern city. There are several small buildings and five castles with connecting tunnels, built from the seventeenth century onwards and now in attractive ruins. Some of them were further damaged by British bombardment during the last war.

In one building there is an exhibition of rather crudely made pottery. One piece is shaped like an Easter egg: when you take the lid off there are Solomon and the Queen of Sheba in bed together.

We are back for sunset and drinks and a conversation about the Royal Family: "I blame the Queen Mother," says the Cheltenham Widow.

Wednesday: Gonder – Bahir Dar

We are into the sixth day of this tour, and I know people will be scratchy and complaining. For some reason it always happens just before the half-way mark and tomorrow we will be over the watershed and everyone will cheer up and start looking forward to going home. Someone once told me it was a sort of syndrome and there is a name for it.

Sure enough, Lady Bracknell is grumbling that she can't get up in the morning because she goes to bed too early. The Cheltenham Widow doesn't like her room again, and Worried John has had problems with the plumbing in his. Miss Welleby is still dying, but insists on taking a taxi to see one of the churches she missed yesterday. The taxi has GOD IS LOVE on a sticker in the back window which is reassuring if we don't see her again.

We do, and all set off in bus for the four-hour drive back to Bahir Dar. "Dust in the eyes and the ears and the nose, dust in the hair and dust between the toes." Lovely to be back with Greensleeves in the Lake Tana hotel.

The Earnest Widow whispers that she is concerned about Silent Sheila, as she has had pneumonia nine times and can recognise it when she sees it.

After lunch we drive up to Haile Selassie's palace which looks like a building from Welwyn Garden City – a vast suburban villa with views across the town to Lake Tana. Then we stand and admire the nearby (disputed) source of Blue Nile.

Some of us are feeling under-exercised and so we decide to walk the half-mile through jacaranda trees in full purple blossom, down the hill to the bridge over the river. "Look out for crocodiles, hippos, and kingfishers," says the guide-book. No sign.

By now everyone is getting fed up with the "minders" who attach themselves to us wherever we go, and try and help whether we want it or not. "I am a student. My father and mother are dead. Give me money to pay for my schooling." They seize our wrists and tie them with woollen bracelets in Rastafarian colours.

Thursday: Bahir Dar

It is overcast and cloudy for our boat trip on Lake Tana. Miss Welleby must be feeling better as she is giving brother a lot of stick (he spends most of his time reading or asleep). We visit two monasteries on small islands. One has a delightful fresco of Pharaoh's army pursuing the Israelites across the Red Sea with helmets bobbing in the water and swords and muskets waving about. The second monastery has much-restored frescoes and too many minders swarming round. Worried John's camera is full of sand and has packed up, but Chris Graham comes to the rescue with a miniature hoover which sucks out the dust.

We picnic on dried-up chicken, bread, oranges and fizzy water, and board the boat for the five hour return voyage. Everyone, except snoozing Welley, soon gets bored and feels chilled, hoping against hope for a nice hot bath when we get back. No such luck.

Friday: Bahir Dar

Off to Tis Abay Falls – one of Ethiopia's most popular tourist attractions and the main reason Worried John came to Ethiopia. (I've read other Tour Leaders' reports on these, and hope he won't be disappointed).

It's a twenty minute walk uphill from the bus to the Falls, and half-way up Corn-crake is told she must pay seven dollars for her video if she brings it any further. There is a scene and I offer to take it back for her – any excuse for some exercise – and am accompanied by officials to make sure I leave it on the bus. I soon catch up the others who are huffing and puffing their way up the hill with Silent Sheila gasping for breath. Lady Bracknell (beekeeper's hat on head) is purple in the face. Nine-times-pneumonia Earnest Widow is wheezing, and as for Welley – I have to do a Sir Philip Sidney with my water bottle as he creeps his way up, stopping every few inches. The twenty minute stroll takes an hour and a half.

Luckily Worried John is thrilled by the water trickling over the edge of the waterfall, though the much-travelled Grahams say it's not a patch on the Victoria Falls.

Then it's time for the walk back which takes just as long. Welley isn't going to make it as he is miles behind the others, but fortunately one of the many minders offers him a donkey and he rides triumphantly up to the bus. No palm leaves, but nevertheless, Hosanna in the Highest. Miss Welleby is livid: "Trust him. It's me that has been ill." She swears never to go on holiday with him again.

After lunch we walk through the dusty town and watch reed-boat builders at work in their boat yard. Each boat takes several hours to make, and then lasts for about four weeks. It is very skilled work, and the Grahams are in their element with no video restrictions. Then we go to the post-office to buy stamps. It is a small concrete building – just like any other post office inside, with counters and grills and long queues. The Earnest Widow is upset because Gabriel queue barges for us. The Grahams want to buy one of every single Ethiopian stamp which takes for ever.

The Cheltenham Widow is very worried about Silent Sheila. She arranges flowers in a hospice and can recognise cancer when she sees it.

Saturday: Bahir Dar – Lalibela

Today is Lalibela, the highlight of our tour: famous for its thirteen rock churches hewn out of bed-rock eight hundred years ago. Their excavation is somewhat of a mystery and their origin clouded in legend. Until recently they were little known outside Ethiopia, but now they are World Heritage Sites and very much on the tourist map, although they are living Christian churches and the centre of village life.

It is an early flight with the usual searches and frisks, and then we go by bus along the incredibly rough road up to Lalibela. The driver goes like a bat out of hell, apologising for not going faster on account of a flat tyre.

Our government run hotel stands on its own about a mile away from the town in a rather bleak sandy landscape. There is something I don't like about this hotel, and although it's exactly the same as all the others it gives me the creeps.

After lunch we set off to look at the churches. So far, the only halt and sick we have seen have been in our own party, but here they are lined up by the gates – blind, deformed, leprous, and missing limbs. There are young children and old men and women all standing silently begging for alms.

Corn-crake is asked for ten dollars for the video and she flies off the handle in front of all these people, making my favourite remark that no tour is complete without: "I don't mind, but it's the principle of the thing."

There are about fifteen huge churches here and many more in the surrounding mountainside. We go up and down steps, along narrow ledges, through passages and tunnels. There is nothing green; no grass, no trees, just solid rock. Welley suddenly says "I must pee, now" and does. He gets a frightful ticking off from our minder who says this is a very holy place and no one does that sort of thing. Miss Welleby disowns him.

It is pitch dark inside the churches, but luckily the Grahams have brought an enormous searchlight.

Silent Sheila is in a state of collapse and can't walk another step. I suggest that the minders carry her, but obviously this is not done, and they drag her back to the bus.

I am feeling really tired with the strain of worrying about these sickly clients, and go up to bed early. I turn on the light over the basin and there is a terrific explosion. The light bulb explodes with force, shooting glass ten feet into the room missing me by millimetres. I spend ages picking tiny shards out of my sponge bag, my bedclothes and the carpet, and can't sleep at all after that, but such a relief it was me and not one of the others. A truly shattering experience.

Sunday: Lalibela

It's an early start and a mule ride – a rather different sort of tourist attraction – with another rock church at the end to give it a point.

The three weakest clients decide not to come, thank goodness. Everyone is uncomfortable on the mules, except the Cheltenham Widow who has taken advice from the Master of the Beaufort (with whom she hunts), and put bubble-wrap over her saddle, and me who seizes the opportunity to walk the ten miles rather than ride.

It is stunningly beautiful country, with layer after layer of "blue-remembered" mountains stretching into the distance. There are villages with picturesque mud huts and simple stockades for animals and no television aerials, or pylons. One enterprising woman has put up a notice outside her hut: "Queen of Sheba's Tea Rooms," and she sits on a wooden stool with an old black kettle simmering away on a fire of sticks.

We keep going and approach the edge of a ravine where we start walking down a hundred and fifty steps to the rock church below, but we get muddled up with a silent funeral procession coming up towards us. Everyone looks longingly at the bed being carried from the church by several men, but Archangel explains it is for a dead body (absit omen).

Back onto the mules for the journey back. Lady Bracknell decides to walk, but only for five minutes thank goodness, since she crawls along. She is very wobbly on her mule though, so I have to walk beside her, steadying her as she lurches from side to side, terrified that her huge bulk will come crashing down on top of me.

We have a dismal lunch at the hotel and then go off to view the remaining rock churches. Welley asks if they will be different or just more of the dark. Corncrake is terrifically popular with the priests as she takes photographs of them with her Polaroid camera and gives them the instant result.

Back at the hotel I have a drink with a young English doctor attached to another group. He has noticed our three invalids puffing and wheezing and asks me not to tell them that he is a chest specialist from Nottingham.

There is a folk show after dinner and I am very, very unpopular with the organiser as I said we would watch it, but everyone is exhausted and goes to bed except the Earnest Widow and me. My bedroom lights don't work – the manager was uninterested in my explosion – but the full moon streaming in is far better than the candles he couldn't find.

Tomorrow we are leaving here and flying to Axum – the final stop on our journey before we head back to Addis.

Monday: Lalibela – Axum

Worried John has been sick all night. There is no water in his bathroom and he describes every detail of his condition – why on earth do people think you want to hear? But of course it's my job to listen and sympathise.

There are the usual endless searches at Lalibela airport and the flight is delayed. Most of the aircraft flying to these small towns have trebled in size but the airport buildings and facilities haven't expanded, so they find it difficult to cope with the extra number of passengers.

We arrive at Axum and find our hotel with rooms in the usual conformation, but this time round a courtyard – with an empty swimming pool, of course, in the middle of it. There are enormous, fluffy white bath towels in the bathrooms, but no water to go with them.

Axum is the oldest city in Ethiopia, and the holiest centre of the Ethiopian Orthodox church. The Ark of the Covenant, which disappeared from Jerusalem in the sixth century BC was believed to have been taken to the Maryam Tsion church in Axum, where it lies under lock and key to this day.

We visit the field of stelae – giant pre-Christian obelisks carved out of granite, as memorials to ancient rulers. The tallest of them fell over several centuries ago, and the next tallest was pinched by the Italians and remains in Rome.

Everybody walks round like zombies, exhausted by heat and dust and we are thankful to stop for tea in the nearby Axum hotel, which would like our company's custom. There is a huge satellite dish in the middle of the pretty garden, and a huge television set on the terrace belting out news of Saddam Hussein. There is a huge television set in every poky bedroom. I think I won't recommend it.

There is a bad moment at dinner when Miss Welleby says that the Falklands should be given back to Argentina. "And Gibraltar to Spain?" "Certainly, and Northern Ireland to the republic."

Tuesday: Axum

I have an early breakfast alone with Silent Sheila who talks for the first time. She left her husband because he didn't talk to her for a year. "Do you work?" I ask. "Yes, don't tell the others, but I am a doctor at Exeter General Hospital." I nearly fall off my chair in amazement.

I decide to call the rather slimy manager's bluff and tell him that if we don't get any hot water tonight I will recommend that our company stays at the Axum hotel in future.

We are going to Yeha to see its ruined temple. It's a long, breathtakingly beautiful drive through pastures, fertile valleys and rugged mountains. The Earnest Widow annoys the others by going on about feeling guilty being a tourist in this poor country, while they just want to sit and enjoy the scenery.

Yeha is an ancient ruined city founded at about the same time as Axum. The temple is colossal and its well preserved state may be explained by its conversion to a church after Axum adapted to Christianity.

Miss Welleby hasn't come, so Welley – let off the hook – sleeps all the way there and back and doesn't get out of the bus to look at the temple.

We pass the site of the famous Battle of Adwa – a huge open space and Archangel Gabriel tells us proudly that in 1896 a hundred thousand Ethiopians defeated twenty thousand Italians.

Back to Axum and more sightseeing after lunch. The Queen of Sheba's bath is a large pool made from a dam, with views over the stelae field. Then the church which holds the Ark of Covenant – never seen by anyone except its guardian. It is the third church to be built on the site – the other two were destroyed – and this one built (rather wisely) like a battlemented castle, with visitors kept well away behind railings. Welley points to a battered yellow tin box hanging on a wall. "Bet that's where they keep the Ark," he says.

The hotel manager says that a huge party of Spaniards (who have been dogging our footsteps the whole week) has arrived, and he will put on the hot water fifteen minutes early especially for us. "I will cheat the Spaniards," he says with glee. Everyone stands by their taps, ready to turn them on. Twenty-five minutes later lukewarm water trickles through.

There is big excitement at dinner. The Patriarch of Addis Ababa, tall and bearded, walks in followed by his retinue of bishops and other clergy, and sits at the table beside us, creating an atmosphere that makes us all sit up straight and talk self-consciously to our neighbours.

The slimy manager insists I have a drink with him after dinner, but I manage to slip past while he is watching football on the television.

Wednesday: Axum – Addis Ababa

All set to leave the hotel at 8am, but catch sight of the Spaniards trying to depart at the same time. Our elderly party springs into action and gets to the airport before them. Our luggage is examined and re-examined and the Cheltenham Widow's bottle of Pimm's, and Chris's whisky is confiscated. (A plane was recently hi-jacked by two men with bottles wrapped in handkerchiefs looking like guns.)

We have a two hour wait for our flight at the usual tin-shack departure lounge. It is very hot and there is no shade, but at least we have seats – on a wooden bench. The Cheltenham Widow is keen to play bridge, but only two takers. The flight is late, but we eventually arrive at Addis – having stopped to re-fuel on the way. Back at the Hilton we have blissful, blissful hot water and clean baths.

Most spend the afternoon in the garden or swimming pool, but the Grahams (three hundred photographs under their belts) insist on taking Gebre to the Folk Museum. "Much better than National Museum that we went to on the first day." They have been seen most of the sights through the lenses of their cameras and can't wait to get home and bore their friends before setting off on their next holiday.

We have farewell drinks in my room, which overlooks a courtyard where an Ethiopian wedding reception is in full swing. Elegant men and women in dazzling white robes move gracefully among tables covered with damask tablecloths laden with sumptuous-looking food. Jewels sparkle. A band plays. What a contrast with the poverty we have seen in the rest of the country.

Thursday: Addis Ababa – Heathrow

A lie-in at last and another row with the manager about charging us for breakfast. I make him find our invoice and point out ROOMS WITH BREAKFAST written across it. "It doesn't count," he says. "That was added afterwards."

You have to arrive at airports two hours before departure for local flights, but only an hour and a half for international ones. There is panic when our Land Rovers don't arrive to transport us, and they appear too late for comfort, but we needn't have worried. There are long, long queues for the check-in and passport control. Silent Sheila, exhausted, sits on the floor and shuffles along on her bottom. She promises to see her G.P. on her return to England. We have an utterly wonderful flight over the Simien Mountains, across the Red Sea and back, down the Nile to Cairo, Alexandria, Crete and over the Parthenon to land at Athens in the sunset before flying on to Heathrow.

I am very, very relieved that everyone has got home alive.

10 days later

I have a letter from Silent Sheila who was whisked into hospital with pneumonia and pleurisy. Tests on her lungs came back – malignant.

Undaunted, she is off in a fortnight on a voyage to Antarctica.

Prague
I Can Go No Longer

~ December ~

I am on the tube to Heathrow. It is early morning and most of my fellow-travellers are slumped over seats or suitcases, but I am wide awake having been up since 4am. It is the week-end before Christmas and I am going to Prague with my choir, full of grand and forceful people, and I AM NOT IN CHARGE.

I go straight through Terminal 5 and into departures – no need to greet clients and make early morning small-talk, and no need to stand at the check-in desk for two hours ticking lists and waiting for late-comers. No panics about delayed flights, and no responsibilities. I shall fall in with the group and do as I am told.

We arrive in Prague, jump into taxis, and drive through the snow-covered streets to our small hotel near the river.

I am used to bland, modern hotels which have keys laid out at the reception desk so that the check-in takes a few minutes, but this place is chaotic. We are crammed into a small room with everyone talking nineteen to the dozen and the receptionist waving bunches of keys, not knowing who to give them to.

There are complaints about not staying in smart hotels in the Old Town, and I stand back quietly, enjoying that it's not my problem. The hotel is on five floors with two flights of stone steps before you even get to the tiny lift, so it is late afternoon by the time everyone has been allocated rooms, found their luggage, thumped it up the stairs and waited in a queue for the lift. Some, having finally got to their rooms, find them unsatisfactory and start the procedure all over again.

We were only given a small packet of dry biscuits on our flight and we are all hungry, so I am pleased to see a small bar in a brown wrapper on my pillow. Lovely – chocolate. White chocolate. I take a bite and spit it our quickly, realising that it's soap.

The restaurant of the hotel is closed owing to a blizzard that has held up supplies, so we cross the road to a bar full of smokers and smoke, and sit down waiting to be served. We wait and wait. One of our number, an extrovert peer, entertains us by playing carols on a comb and paper napkin – after all this is a musical tour. Eventually we see the menu, order drinks and wait for our food – not sure if it is high-tea or early dinner.

Afterwards I go for a walk with Lady Burton (Romania, "not a hair out of place") who happens to be in the choir. She is draped in furs including long fur boots and I feel drab beside her in my walking boots and old winter coat that saw me through Leningrad all those years ago.

The snow is fresh and deep, and squeaks as we walk along beside the river.

We aim for one of Prague's most prized monuments, the Charles Bridge, its arches floodlit, looking romantic against the night sky. It is nearly seven hundred years old and for a long time was the only bridge across the Vltava. Originally it could take four carriages abreast, but now traffic is banned, and as it's late evening there are no tourists and we walk from side to side admiring the statues that stand on its parapets and the views across to the Old Town. Then up to St Vitus's Cathedral, a huge neo-Gothic building, also floodlit, and towering above us like a giant liner. This is where we are going to join a Czech choir to sing their traditional Christmas Mass, written by an eighteenth century composer called Jan Jakub Ryba.

We walk back over the bridge and through the narrow streets of the Old Town. There are plenty of tourists here because the shops are open, and there are stalls selling pancakes and waffles cooked over charcoal fires, and hot chocolate and mulled wine.

In the Old Square we stand with the cheerful crowds watching the six hundred year old clock strike the hour. As the clock strikes, the twelve apostles pass through an opening in the turret, each one turning towards us and holding up his hand in blessing. Underneath them is an astronomical clock, its face showing a bewildering array of circles and numbers and signs of the zodiac, not meant to tell you the time, but to imitate the orbits of the sun and moon about the Earth.

A loudspeaker blares out Silent Night.

Friday

There are about fifty of us on this choir trip and this morning we are going to see the Wallenstein Palace. First we have breakfast in the cellar basement of our hotel where everyone seems to be on mobiles or studying iPads, or catching up with the Test Match score from Australia on Blackberrys. Someone is ringing home to find out if his dogs are all right. The group meets at Reception in dribs and drabs, no discipline here, and we catch a tram for a ride across the river to the Palace, arriving rather later than planned.

The Palace was built by the Wallenstein family who lived there for four hundred years, until 1945, when it was seized by the state. Today it is the Senate house, and the Archbishop of Prague, together with some of the senators, are going to welcome us. There will then be a press conference followed by a guided tour of the building.

We have to go through security which takes ages, but not as long as it does to remove our coats and hand them to an attendant with a long droopy moustache, who very slowly puts a clothes peg and ticket on every garment. Coats, gloves, hats – all have to have separate pegs. One of the group is wearing a fur coat and she tells me she wants to take it to Harrods to have it repaired, but can't because her son is an Animal Rights campaigner who patrols outside the store with a banner.

At last we are sitting in a large room and the welcoming ceremony begins. It goes slowly as every sentence has to be translated. Welcomes and more welcomes, thanks and more thanks.

Then into another room for the press conference. More welcomes, more translations and more thanks, followed by questions from the press. The Czechs all look smart and urbane in suits and ties, and our chairman, sitting in the middle of them, looks out of place in a tweed jacket and open-necked shirt.

We are falling behind schedule so there is not time for the tour of the palace, and we rush through corridors with frescoes of mythological scenes by Italian artists, neither looking to left nor right.

Back to the cloakroom and clothes pegs are slowly removed from garments. There are a couple of guides waiting to accompany us over the Charles Bridge to the old town, and we set off behind them. But this is an unruly party, and people are more interested in taking photographs and talking amongst themselves rather than listening to a well-informed guide as we battle through the crowds of tourists and trinket-sellers and musical entertainers: quite a contrast with last night.

Time is getting on and when we stop outside a café we hope we are going in for a reviving glass of mulled wine and some lunch, but instead we go into St Francis's Church next door.

First we listen to an organ recital, then to our guide telling us the history of the church: more translations. Apparently it was built for Rome, but picked up and transported here. (Carried by angels?) Next, the museum curator – and owner of the café – tells us all about the museum in the crypt of the church and hopes we will visit it. So do we – and the café. But there is no time. Instead we feel embarrassed by the brown paper bag of presents we are given on leaving: a book about the river, a small mug and a straw angel.

It is now half past two and no mention of lunch. On the tours I lead clients complain we have too much time for lunch and too much to eat: but lunch hasn't been built in to this itinerary, and our next stop is the clock tower in the old town square. We are not going to stand outside with the crowds like last night, but see the inside workings when the clock strikes the hour.

Not being in charge, I don't have to stay with the group, and I slope off with others to a restaurant nearby. Just as we start tucking into hot wine and roast duck, our guide tracks us down and insists that we go with him up several flights of stone steps inside the clock tower. It strikes and we see the apostles revolving. It is not as impressive as seen from the outside with the cheering crowds and we regret our hurried lunch. We go down again quickly as we are going to sing carols to the Mayor at the Old Town Hall next door, and we mustn't keep him waiting. We get there, rush upstairs and stand round a large white and gold reception room holding our carol sheets waiting for the His Worship to appear. He doesn't: "he's much too busy a-signing things." So we sing *Ding Dong Merrily On High* to ourselves. Waiters appear with trays of open sandwiches and glasses of wine which are much appreciated, but not enough, and eaten too quickly, and off we go to rehearse the Christmas Mass – not before we are given another brown paper bag each, containing a huge, heavy book on Czech cubist architecture.

We walk quickly along the slippery pavements, through a dingy entrance, and down several flights of stairs into a small theatre. We have been rehearsing our Czech for ages, but still find it difficult to pronounce the words and fit them to the music.

Afterwards we make our way to a restaurant for dinner, and at last it's time to sit down and relax. A man with a squeeze box appears and recognising an English party starts playing *It's a long way to Tipperary* quickly followed by *My Bonnie lies over the ocean*. That sets us off and we are soon well away with *The Twelve Days of Christmas*, *Good King Wenceslas* of course, and *Silent Night*. We are all singers and are in our element.

Saturday

Free time this morning and everyone scatters, but after lunch those of us who are around walk back over the bridge and up the steep hill, where we have a date at Alphonse Mucha's house for a private visit. We puff and stop and slip all the way up, but are rewarded at the top by wonderful views across the city.

Mucha was an Art Nouveau painter, best known for his posters of beautiful women in flowing classical robes, surrounded by garlands of flowers.

We are met by his daughter-in-law, a very old Scottish lady called Geraldine, who lives alone surrounded by Mucha's works. We walk through one or two formal rooms and then into the more intimate room where she lives. There is a moth-eaten leopard skin complete with head on the floor, a four-poster bed, a grand piano covered in sheets of music – she is also a composer – and a tray laid for tea with a tin of Fortnum's Earl Grey tea. She is very deaf and difficult to talk to, but I was delighted to find that she knew my cousin, a philosophy don at Oxford, who during the communist times used to give lectures to Czech students in secret hide-outs. We thank her enthusiastically and she replies warmly that it's Christmas so people are always dropping in.

Then on to the Cathedral to rehearse with the orchestra and the Czech choir who are performing with us. It is freezing hard – minus fifteen degrees we are told, and the huge building has no heating, so there is no question of our taking off hats, coats, scarves and gloves – and we are still frozen. After the rehearsal we are ushered into a nearby café and fortified with big mugs of mulled wine.

The cathedral is crowded, with people standing in the aisles. You might think that such a huge congregation would warm the building up a bit, but it doesn't and we wonder how the orchestra manages to keep its fingers from going numb. The concert goes well, largely thanks to our Czech singers who sweep us along with them – the music going faster than ever. We can see our breath as we sing; surprised it doesn't freeze in the air.

For once there aren't too may speeches before or afterwards and we enter the Archbishop's Palace next door for refreshments. Up a vast staircase with a red carpet and into magnificent rooms lined with paintings of previous archbishops and cardinals, to be greeted by more mugs of mulled wine. Although the whole congregation seems to be here, there is plenty to eat and drink and we finish the evening by singing our party piece – *Ding Dong Merrily*.

Some wait for taxis and some walk carefully back to the hotel. The snow has melted and re-frozen so it is very slippery underfoot, and on our return we nip down to the cellar restaurant for a hot choc. (before going to bed) and find most of the choir already there. There is a very noisy party of Czechs at the next table. However we are soon in competition, bawling our repertoire of carols at the tops of our voices. Home tomorrow. Happy Christmas everyone.

Sunday

Our suitcases are packed and we are all ready to go. But when we descend into the breakfast cellar we are greeted by long faces. Everyone is on mobiles, Blackberrys or iPads. Heathrow is under snow, all flights are cancelled and there is general panic. The Lords have to get back for a Vote, our conductor has to get to Paris for a concert and I have got another wonderful day in Prague.

Thanks

Thanks first to Jebb, whose gentle wiles
Lured me to walk so many miles:
Then thanks to Arthur at Loose Chippings
Who deftly tidied up these drippings.
Thanks very much to Caroline
Dawnay who read those notes of mine
And got me started on this book.
Thanks to the travel firms who took
Such care that we were seldom stranded,
And if the boat sank, safely landed:
To learned lecturers, who brayed
(Once I had got them on parade)
About the beauties and the history
Of lands that were to all a mystery.
Thanks to every local guide
Who took the weird English in their stride.
But most to customers who thronged
To see the lands for which they longed –
Zestful, delightful, always cheerful
(Or if frustrated, seldom tearful),
All backgrounds, habits, foibles, ages –
Their tolerance, their majestic rages.
Thanks to you all, and come back soon –
We're taking bookings for the Moon.